INTRODUCING TEXTILES & DESIGN

INTRODUCING TEXTILES & DESIGN

Judy Vulker, M.A., B.Sc., Dip. Teach.
Head of Home Economics Department
Queanbeyan High School
•
Helen Cooper, B.A., Dip. Teach.
Head of Home Economics Department
Pendle Hill High School

MACMILLAN
EDUCATION

First published in Australia by
The Macmillan Company of Australia Pty Ltd

First published in Great Britain by
Macmillan Education 1988

Published by
MACMILLAN EDUCATION LTD
Houndmills, Basingstoke, Hampshire RG21 2XS
and London
Companies and representatives
throughout the world

ISBN 0–333–48080–5

Set in Baskerville by
Setrite Typesetters Ltd, Hong Kong
Printed in Hong Kong

Contents

Acknowledgements

We are grateful to the following for permission to reproduce illustrations. (T = top, B = bottom, C = centre, L = left, R = right.)

p. viii: Hong Kong Tourist Association (TR), International Society for Education Information, Tokyo, Inc. (TR), Government of India Tourist Office (BL); p. 1: Koninklijke Instituut van de Tropen, Amsterdam (T), Grace Bros (B); p. 2: Danish Government Tourist Bureau (L), Mansell Collection (R); p. 3: Bernhard Hammerman Furs Pty Ltd; p. 4: Japan National Tourist Organization (CL), Media and Publications Department, University of Melbourne (TR), Herald & Weekly Times Ltd (CBL), National Publicity Studios, Wellington, New Zealand (BR); p. 5: Adidas (Division of Dunlop Olympic Ltd) (L), Bata Shoe Company of Australia Pty Ltd (R); p. 6: Magazine Promotions (TL), Richard McRoberts (TR), Myer Stores Ltd (C and BL), Vogue Australia (CB); p. 7: Rijksmuseum, Amsterdam, for 'Prince William II of Orange and the Princess Mary Stuart' by Anthonie van Dijck (L), Museum of Costume, Assembly Rooms, Bath (R); pp. 13 (T), 14, 15, 24: Simplicity Sewing Machines of Australia; p. 41: Lane Publishing Co. for the photograph from *Knitting Techniques and Projects* (Sunset Books, 1976); Snake Productions Pty Ltd, Melbourne, for the Sols cartoon; p. 46: Sheridan Textiles (L), Murray Book Distributors Pty Ltd, for the photograph from *Cake Decorating Ornaments* by Norma Dunn (1979) (R); pp. 48, 49: John Murray (Publishers) Ltd for two photographs from *Tribal Designs for Needlepoint* by Gay Ann Rogers (1978); p. 53: Andrew Chapman (L), Simplicity & Style Patterns (R); pp. 54–6: Simplicity & Style Patterns; p. 61: Myer Stores Ltd (TC), Qantas Airways Limited (TR), Andrew Chapman (B); p. 63: *Handmade Australia*, summer 1984; p. 67: Margot's Gear (BL), *Powderhound* ski magazine, vol. 9, no. 1, May 1985 (R); p. 71: Andrew Chapman; p. 78: Australian Wool Corporation (R); p. 86: source is *Illustrated Sydney News*, 1876; p. 87: Andrew Chapman (L), Ninette Trading Pty Ltd, Melbourne (R); p. 88: Andrew Chapman; pp. 97–9: based on illustrations in *Folk Costumes from Eastern Europe* by L. M. Fox (Chatto & Windus, 1977); p. 100: Oxford University Press, Melbourne, for the illustration from *Complete Guide to Needlework: Techniques and Materials* by M. Gostelow (1982); p. 103: Bell & Hyman Ltd for two illustrations from *Folkdress of Europe* by James Snowden (1979); pp. 104–6: based on illustrations in *Folk Costumes from Eastern Europe* by L. M. Fox (Chatto & Windus, 1977); p. 106: Oxford University Press for the illustration from *Complete Guide to Needlework: Techniques and Materials* by M. Gostelow.

While every care has been taken to trace and acknowledge copyright, the publishers tender their apologies for any accidental infringement where they have been unable to do so. They would be pleased to come to a suitable arrangement with the rightful owner in each case.

Preface

Introducing Textiles & Design has been written for junior secondary courses in Textiles and Design. It provides a vital and interesting introduction to a subject that is becoming increasingly popular in the wake of superseded Needlework courses.

While the text is aimed primarily at Years 1 and 2, some of the practical activities are suitable for Year 3 and 4 students with little previous background in the subject.

With today's teenagers in mind, we have taken a multicultural view of textiles, examining the various cultural influences in textiles, arts and design. The text and practical activities are designed to appeal to both boys and girls. The activities require only basic skills, and all items can be made relatively quickly, so that a high level of interest is maintained and satisfaction gained.

Basic information for students' reference, such as the parts of the sewing machine, how to load a bobbin case, textile tools and embroidery stitches, is clearly set out and illustrated. Learning experiences are graduated from Chapter 1 through to Chapter 11. Many of the activities in the last chapter, which is devoted solely to activities, require skills learnt in the other ten chapters. Extension activities are included for more advanced students, as well as those in elective classes.

In developing the material, we have taken account of the different approaches to Textiles and Design courses taken by individual schools and in different states.

Judy Vulker and Helen Cooper

Where this book is used in the UK, teachers should refer to the Citizens' Advice Bureaux or the Consumers' Association rather than the Australian Consumer Affairs Bureau, and the British Standards Institution rather than the Australian Standards Association.

1

Fashion

Clothes of different societies

The photographs in Fig. 1.1 show people from different countries. You can tell a lot about the lives these people lead and the jobs they do by observing the kinds of clothes they wear.

People wear different clothes for different occasions, depending on such things as:

- **The Weather** — To protect our bodies from changing temperatures, wind, rain and sun, we wear different clothes. In winter, warm woollen jumpers are worn. If you live in an area where it snows, jumpers will not be warm enough and you will need a parka. In hot climates, people need clothes to keep cool. In Australia shorts and T-shirts are worn to keep cool but in really hot climates, long flowing robes are needed.
- **The Time of Day** — During the day, people do a number of different activities and so the clothes needed will change. Students often wear a uniform to school and Scouts and Guides have special uniforms.

  When wearing special clothes, people tend to act the way other people expect them to act. What would you expect the following people to do?
  (a) Person in school uniform.
  (b) Athlete in track suit.
  (c) Nurse.
  (d) Police officer.

Fig. 1.1 Clothes of different societies (opposite)

Fig. 1.2 Clothing worn in Bali and Australia

When people put clothes on and act a certain way, it is said they are performing a role.

- **Where People Live** — Clothes show the society in which a person lives. For instance, the clothes worn by people in Bali, an island of Indonesia, are often different from clothes worn in Australia (see Fig. 1.2).

Activity 1:1

Clothes show different situations and different cultures.

You will need

- Old magazines or travel brochures.
- Glue and scissors.

Method

(1) Collect 5 illustrations of dress. Paste into your notebook.
(2) In 2–3 sentences describe the clothes the people are wearing.
(3) Where would the clothes be worn?

The first clothes

People did not need clothes many thousands of years ago, as they lived in warm climates. When people moved to other areas or lands they needed clothes.

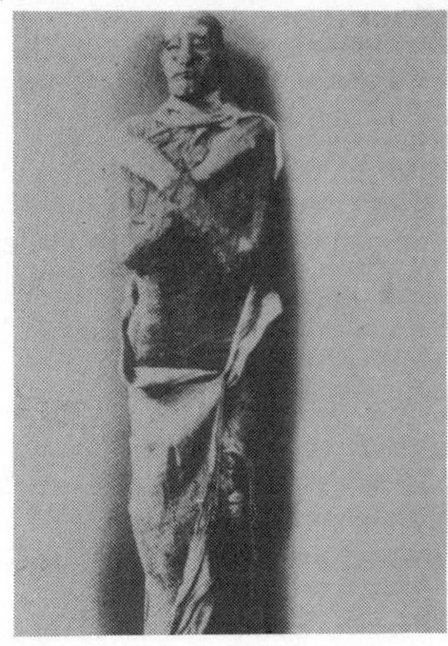

Fig. 1.3 Peat bog man and an Egyptian mummy

Clothes protect the body and keep it warm. Animal skins were first used for this purpose.

Eventually people wanted more than skins of animals to cover their bodies. Plants and animals provided the fibres to make cloth. Examples of early cloth include mummy wrappings from Egypt and clothing from the Bronze and Iron Ages found in peat bog burials in Denmark (Fig. 1.3). The people and their clothing buried in the bogs of Denmark were preserved by the peat so we can see today how they lived. The length of time clothing lasted in these countries depended on the climate. Because Denmark has a cold climate, clothes did not deteriorate.

After school each person does different activities and so they do not need the same clothes.

Activity 1:2

In your workbook, copy the chart shown in Fig. 1.4. List the activities you do. (The first activity is done as an example.) Then answer the following questions.

(1) When you change clothes, do you belong to a different group?
(2) How do the clothing needs of a soccer player and a scout differ?
(3) What clothing needs do they have?
(4) What clothes do you need to have in your wardrobe?
*Do not forget to plan for your underwear.

Activities	Clothes needed	Reasons why these clothes are worn
School student	School uniform	Identify with school. They are comfortable.

Fig. 1.4 Different clothes for different needs

What clothes do people need?

What clothes do people really need?

Often we have enough clothes to wear but we want more. The reasons may be:

- Friends have new clothes.
- People want to have the same clothes as friends.
- People enjoy buying new clothes.
- People enjoy wearing fashionable clothes.

How can you get the clothes you need?

Buying all your clothes can be expensive so why not make some of them?

Today, people wear casual clothing to many places and clothes such as sloppy joes, shorts, skirts and shirts are easy to make. Making clothes saves money, is fun and means that you have more outfits to choose from!

Reasons for wearing clothing styles

Clothing is one of the first things you notice about a person. Clothes create a first impression.

Later, facial features, hair, mannerisms and voice will also be noticed. When you first meet someone, you often decide if you like them or not. Later, as you get to know them, you may change your mind. First impressions do not always last.

While at school, people dress the same as their peer group. People want to belong to a group. As children grow up, they learn the attitudes and values of their family and culture.

Attitudes and values are reflected in the clothing people wear (Fig. 1.5, below and p. 4). The clothes you wear show what you value.

Fig. 1.5 People have different values

Activity 1:3

(1) Look at 20 people in the shopping centre. Describe in 2–3 sentences what they are wearing.
(2) Clothes often reveal people's values. Judging by their clothing, what values do you think are important to the people you observed?

Customs and traditions

Customs and traditions influence the clothes people wear. Some clothes have had little or no change of style for centuries. These include:

- Kimonos.
- Academic dress.
- Robes and headdresses worn by nuns and monks.
- National dress.

Fig. 1.6 Some clothes have not changed in style for centuries.

Influence of family, friends and community

The first influence on the type of clothes a person wears is the family. As children get older, friends also influence dress. Sometimes parents do not like the way their children dress.

When people leave school, dress styles may change again. This is because people have more money to buy clothes. Dress styles worn by a person reflect their personality and the influence of other people.

Fig. 1.7 Advertising has created a demand for fashionable clothes.

Influence of changing social conditions

Advertising in newspapers, magazines and on television has created a demand for clothes. People want to buy the new fashions. The increase in the use of credit cards means that people can buy now and pay later and some people may buy clothes they cannot really afford.

Influence of age on clothes

Clothing needs vary from age group to age group (Fig. 1.6). In each age group people wear clothes to meet their particular needs. Babies and young children need clothes to be comfortable, *efficient* and easy to take on and off. Clothes need to be cheap as children grow quickly.

In primary and high schools, clothes reflect the changes people go through as they search for their own identity. Clothes still need to be comfortable and efficient to wear, but at this stage it is also important that clothes conform with those worn by people of the same age. Wearing the same clothes as friends increases self confidence.

Adolescents or teenagers begin to need clothes which make them confident about themselves. At a certain age, clothes are often chosen that will attract the opposite sex.

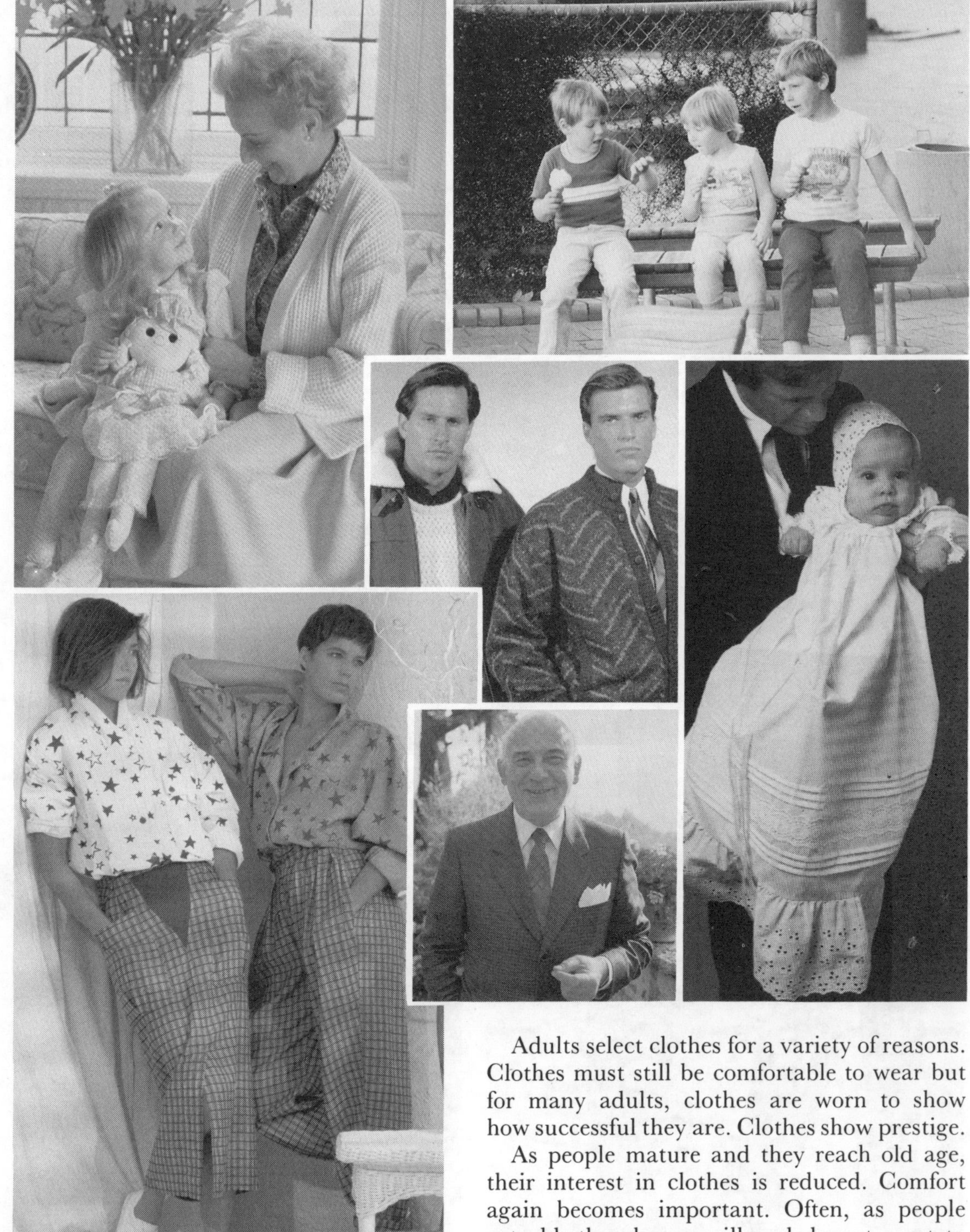

Fig. 1.8 People of different ages choose different types of clothing.

Adults select clothes for a variety of reasons. Clothes must still be comfortable to wear but for many adults, clothes are worn to show how successful they are. Clothes show prestige.

As people mature and they reach old age, their interest in clothes is reduced. Comfort again becomes important. Often, as people get old, they become ill and do not want to bother with tight fitting or fashionable clothes. When people retire, they may have to rely on the Aged Persons' Pension, and they often have less money to spend on clothes.

What clothes are fashionable

Each season, clothing styles change. What is in fashion this season?

Changing fashion keeps us interested in clothes. The manufacturers and designers of clothes like to change clothing styles. As styles change, people buy them and the manufacturers and designers make a profit.

Consumers have the final say in fashion for they buy the clothing. If they do not buy fashion clothing, then it will not be popular and a profit will not be made.

Activity 1:4

(1) In your workbook, under the heading *Phrases that describe me*, write the sentences that best describe you. If you want to add extra descriptions, do so at the bottom of the list.

- I like to wear the same clothes as my friends.
- I want to be different.
- Clothes are not important.
- I don't spend money on clothes.
- I follow fashion.
- I need to be accepted.
- I want to show my shape.
- My parents tell me what to wear.
- I get ideas about clothes from people in the street.
- I want to dress like my favourite television or pop star.
- My friends dress that way.
- I like getting gear that is advertised.
- I like to attract others.
- I like to be different.
- Colour is important to me.

(2) (a) Collect pictures of the current fashion.

(b) In your workbook, describe the styles selected.

(c) On the noticeboard, under the heading *What clothes are fashionable*, each student should pin up one example of a current fashion and briefly describe its features to the class.

(d) *Discussion*: What are the general features of the styles on the noticeboard?

Fig. 1.9 Fashions from (left) the seventeenth and (right) the mid-nineteenth centuries

Activity 1:5

Look very carefully at the photographs of past fashions (Fig. 1.7). Write a paragraph about each style.

(1) Describe the clothes.
(2) What sort of life would these people have led?
(3) Do the clothes give any ideas as to what society was like at the time?

Words to remember

occasions	attitudes	personality
protect	values	advertising
role	customs	prestige
mummy	traditions	
fashionable	kimono	
impression	academic	
mannerisms		

Glossary

Occasion — A special time or event.
Impression — The way you want other — people see you. The impression created may not always be the one you want to create.
Attitude — The way a person thinks or behaves.
Values — Things that are important to people.
Customs — A way of behaving in a country.
Traditions — Beliefs or customs handed down from one generation to the next.
Personality — Characteristics of a person.
Prestige — Respect from having a good job, good reputation or being a high achiever.

Activity 1:6 Extension

(1) Unscramble the letters to find items that have been discussed in this chapter. The first letter of each word is printed in **bold**.
   (a) **O**CCIONSA
   (b) ION**F**ASH
   (c) THE**C**LOS
   (d) TUDES**A**TTI
   (e) UES**V**AL
   (f) OMS**C**UST
   (g) **T**RADSIONIT

(2) Use each word you have unscrambled in a sentence.

2

Textile tools

Tools for textiles

Scissors

Paper scissors are used for cutting paper patterns and designs.

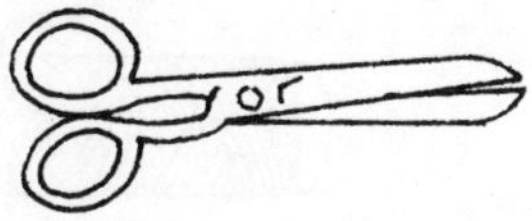

Fig. 2.1

Fabric scissors (Fig. 2.2) are much sharper than paper scissors and are used for cutting out fabrics only.

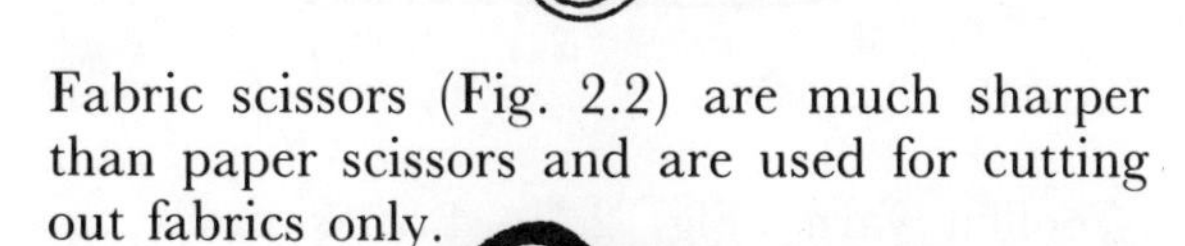

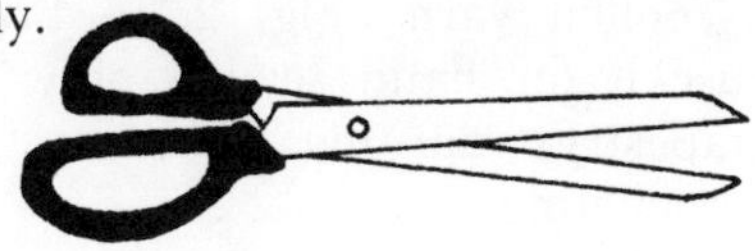

Fig. 2.2

Embroidery scissors (Fig. 2.3) are small scissors used for hand sewing. They have fine, sharp ponts.

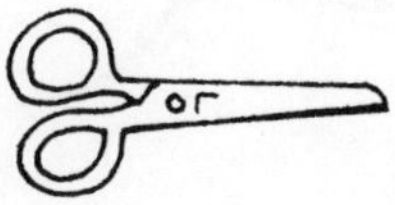

Fig. 2.3

Pinking shears (Fig. 2.4) are used to cut fabrics which do not fray easily.

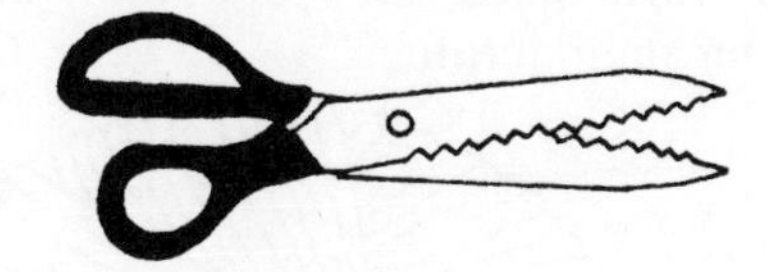

Fig. 2.4

Pins

Sewing pins (Fig. 2.5) are sharp, short pins which will go through two layers of fabric easily.

Fig. 2.5

Berry pins (Fig. 2.6) are long pins with large heads for thicker fabrics.

Fig. 2.6

Needles

Crewels (Fig. 2.7) are easy-to-thread needles which are sharp enough for hand sewing and embroidery.

Fig. 2.7

Sharps (Fig. 2.8) are long, thin needles with a small eye for fine hand sewing.

Fig. 2.8

Tapestry needles (Fig. 2.9) are large, thick needles with a large eye for thick yarn-like wool.

Fig. 2.9

Darning needles (Fig. 2.10) are longer than tapestry needles with a large eye for mending woollen clothing.

Fig. 2.10

Bodkins (Fig. 2.11) are large needles with a very blunt point and large eye used for threading ribbon, elastic or cord through openings or hems.

Fig. 2.11

Tape measure

Tape measures (Fig. 2.12) are made of soft fibreglass and are used for measuring fabric and seams. They are marked in millimetres and centimetres.

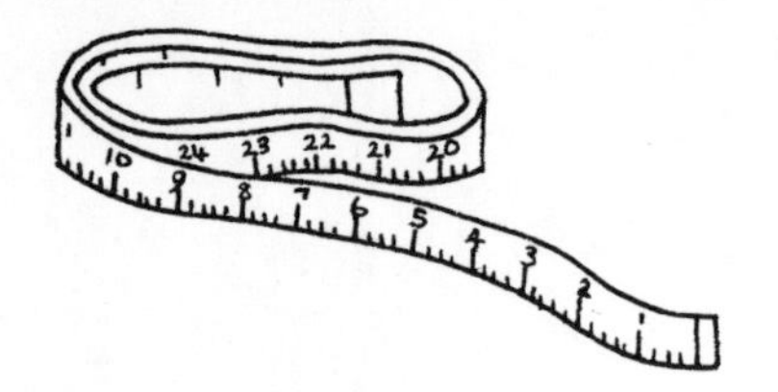

Fig. 2.12

Fabric markers

All fabric markers wash out easily with water and detergent.

Carbon (Fig. 2.13) is placed on the wrong side of fabric to mark out a pattern.

Fig. 2.13

Marking pencils (Fig. 2.14) are chalk pencils for marking patterns or cutting lines on fabric.

Fig. 2.14

Marking chalk (Fig. 2.15) is flat piece of chalk which comes in many colours.

Fig. 2.15

Unpicker

An unpicker is used to unpick machining which has been incorrectly sewn.

Fig. 2.16

Thread

Mercerised cotton (Fig. 2.17) is thread which has been strengthened for machine sewing and should be used only for cotton fabrics.

Fig. 2.17

Polyester thread is used with any synthetic fabric or fabric made from natural fibres such as cotton or wool. This is a very strong thread.

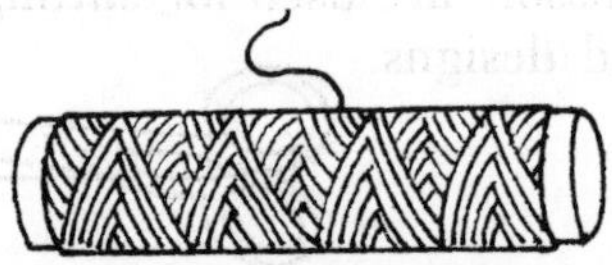

Fig. 2.18

Woollen yarn (Fig. 2.19) breaks easily, so use it for hand sewing only. It is used for tapestry, darning, knitting, weaving and crocheting.

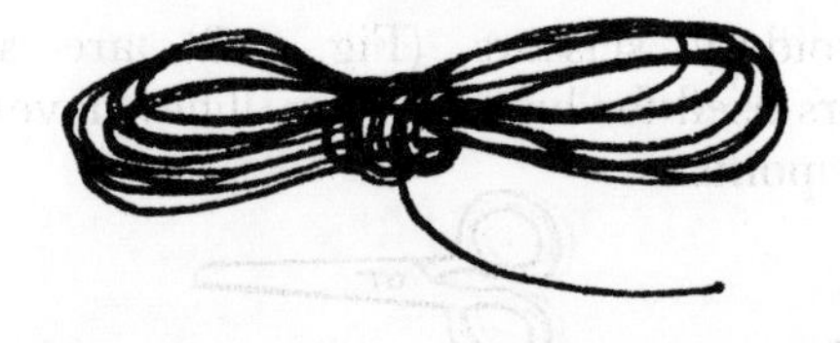

Fig. 2.19

Macramé jute (Fig. 2.20) is strong, thick, rough yarn used for rope and decorative knotting or macramé.

Fig. 2.20

Weaving looms

There are many different types of weaving looms. These are used to make fabric, from one centimetre wide to 150 centimetres. The following are examples of the hand looms which you may have at school.

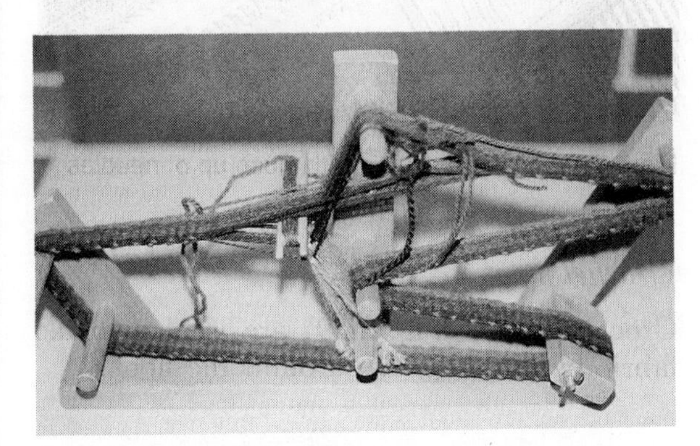

Fig. 2.21 Inkle loom

Fig. 2.22 4-shaft loom

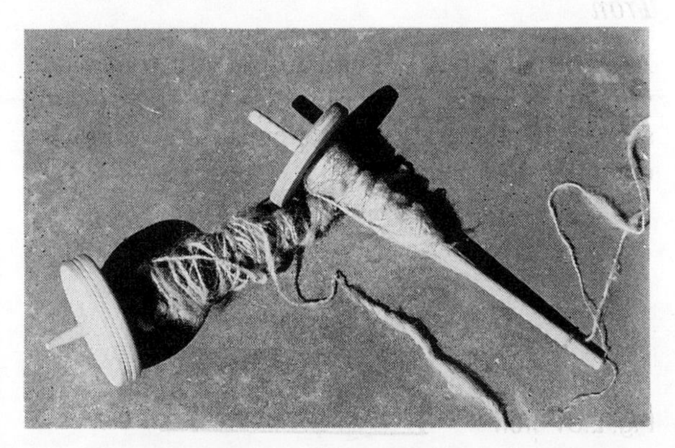

Fig. 2.23 Drop spindle

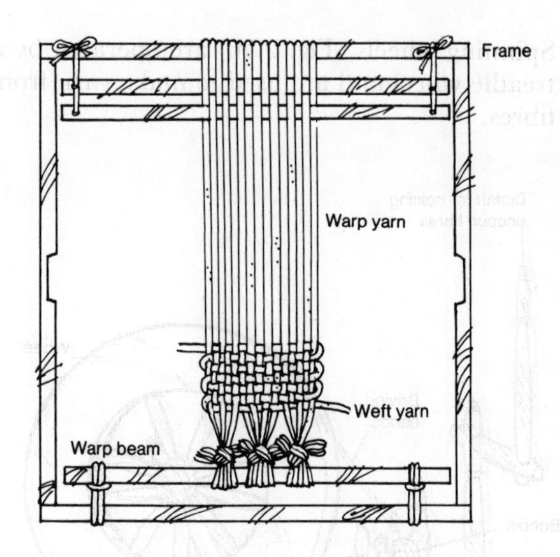

Fig. 2.24 Back strap loom

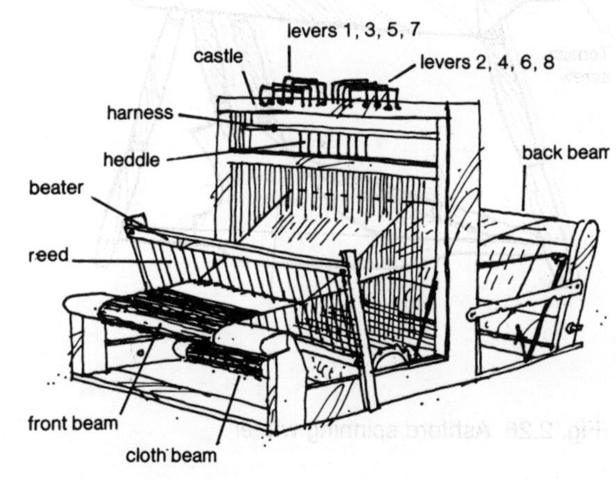

Fig. 2.25 8-shaft loom

Spinning apparatus

Drop spindles (Fig. 2.23) are used in drop spinning. This is one of the oldest types of hand spinning. Fibres are drawn out, then spun into thread or yarn by twisting the spindle.

Spinning wheels (Fig. 2.26) are operated by a treadle wheel and are used to make yarn from fibres.

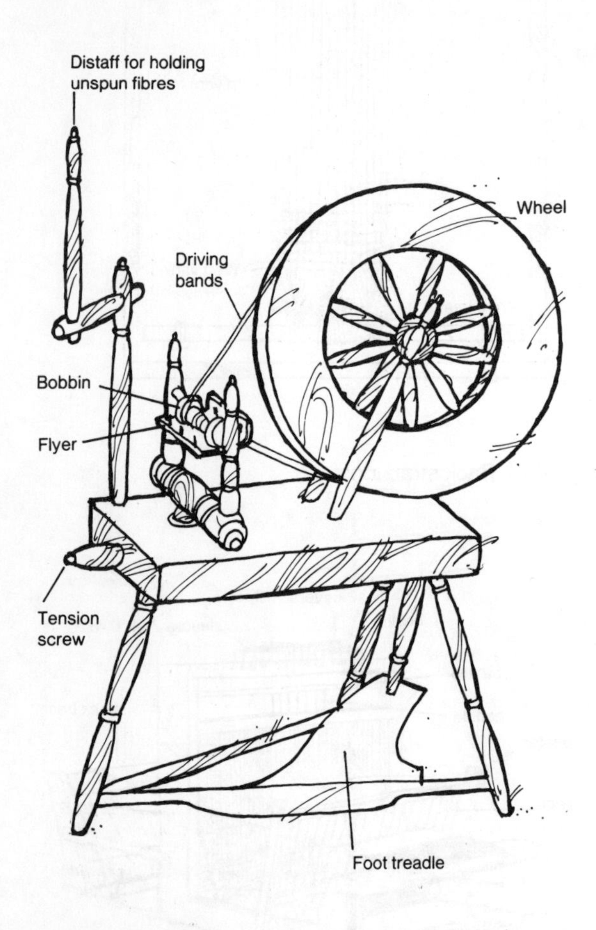

Fig. 2.26 Ashford spinning wheel

Knitting needles

Knitting needles (Figs. 2.27 and 2.28) are usually made of plastic or steel. They may be used to make fabric by hand or machine knitting.

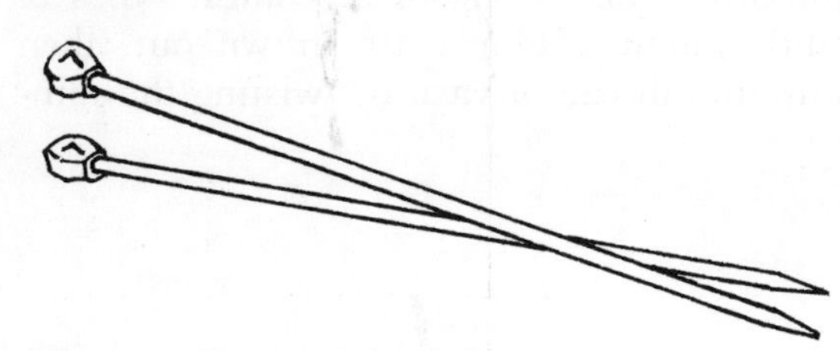

Fig. 2.27 Hand knitting needles

Fig. 2.28 Knitting machine with close up of needles

Crochet hook

Crochet hooks (Fig. 2.29) are used to make fabric by looping yarn around the hook.

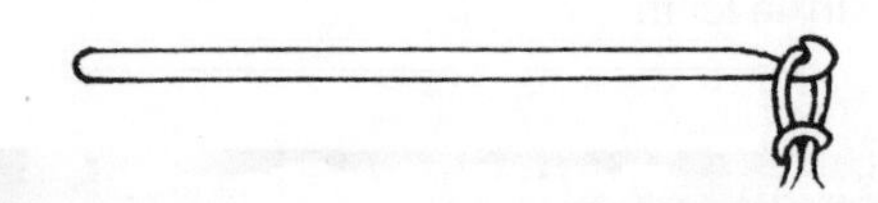

Fig. 2.29 Crochet hook looping a yarn

Fabric glue

This glue (Fig. 2.30) is a useful item for pasting felt and fabrics to be appliquéd.

Fig. 2.30 Fabric glue

Iron

An iron (Fig. 2.31) is an important tool when you are sewing. You must always press your sewing well after each step if you want to ensure a good finish.

Fig. 2.31 Iron

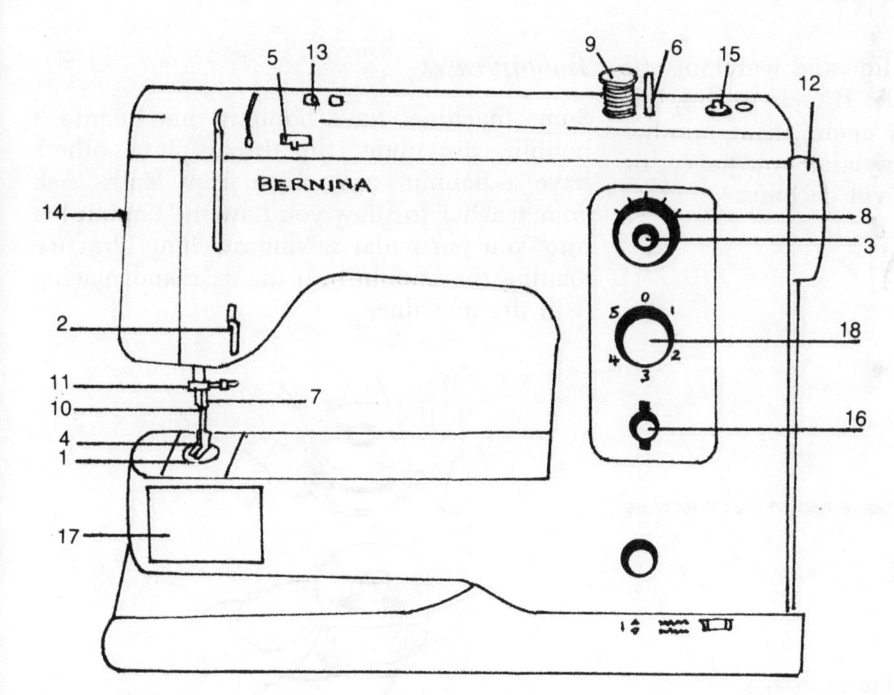

Parts of the sewing machine

1 Throat plate
2 Thread guide
3 Stitch width control
4 Feed teeth
5 Tension control
6 Spool pin
7 Presser foot
8 Stitch length control
9 Thread
10 Needle
11 Needle clamp
12 Balance wheel
13 Stitch selector
14 Thread take-up lever
15 Bobbin winder
16 Reverse stitch control
17 Bobbin case shutter
18 Buttonhole dial

Fig. 2.32 A Bernina sewing machine

Sewing machine

It is important to identify parts of the sewing machine (Fig. 2.32) before you start to use it. Check the parts carefully and make sure you know the function of each part before you start sewing.

Activity 2:1

Trace the machining practice sheet (Fig. 2.33) from your book. Now it's your turn to do some machining! First of all, try without thread to see how careful you can be and follow the lines on your practice sheet.

To turn a corner, sew slowly to the corner, making sure that the needle is in the fabric. Raise the presser foot, turn the fabric so that the presser foot is facing the correct way for sewing the next line, then lower the presser foot and continue to sew.

Using the sample lines, practise keeping to the lines by lifting the presser foot when you need to make a turn. The curved lines can be sewn without lifting the presser foot.

Try to follow one of the *guide lines* on the *throat plate* (Fig. 2.34) by keeping the edge of

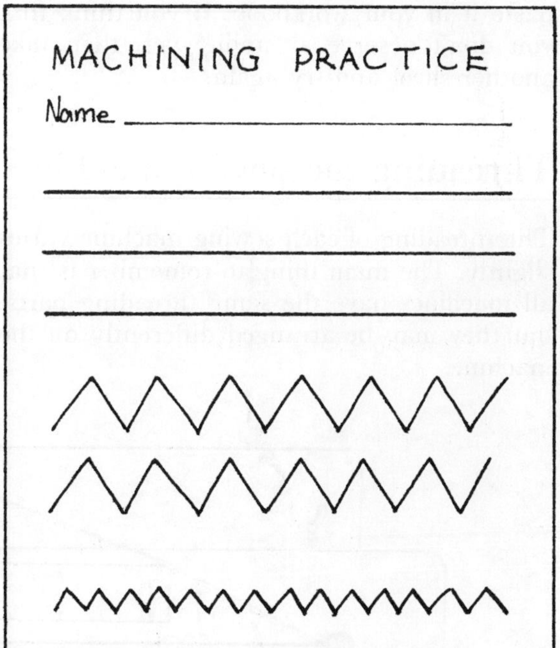

MACHINING PRACTICE

Name ______________________

Fig. 2.33 Machining practice sheet

the paper on the guide line and watching the line instead of the needle. If your sewing line wasn't very straight, try again, using another guide line. The more practice you have, the better your machining will become.

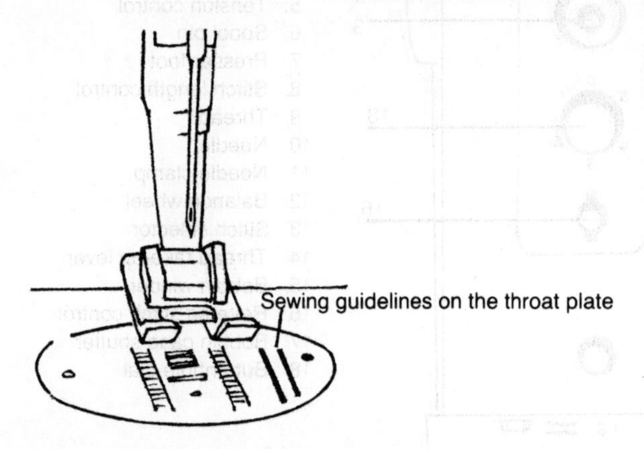

Fig. 2.34 Throat plate showing guide lines

Ask your teacher to sign your work, then paste it in your workbook. If you think that you don't deserve a 'smilie' yet, then take another sheet and try again.

Threading the sewing machine

The threading of each sewing machine varies slightly. The main thing to remember is that all machines have the same threading parts, but they may be arranged differently on the machine.

Bobbin cases

Some machines have bobbins that fit into a bobbin case under the throat plate, others have a bobbin case which front loads. Ask your teacher to show you how the bobbin fits into your particular sewing machine. Practice loading the bobbin into the case and placing it in the machine.

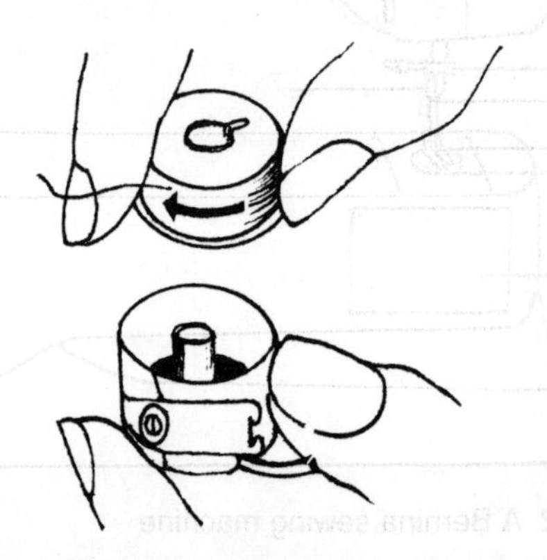

Fig. 2.35 Bobbin and bobbin case for a Bernina machine

Filling the bobbin

- Place the thread to be used on a spool pin.
- Place the bobbin on the bobbin winder.
- Take the thread and wind it around the bobbin a few times to secure it.
- Unlock the balance wheel by holding the centre and turning the outside wheel anti-clockwise.
- Press your foot on the foot control.

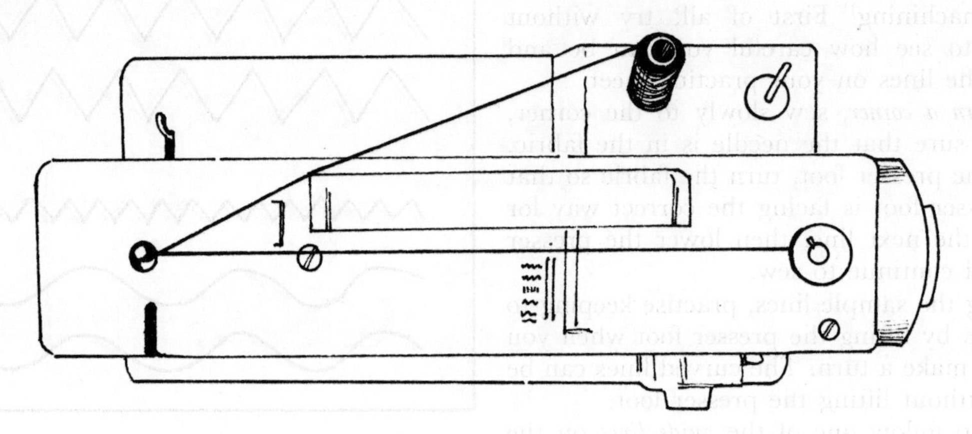

Fig. 2.36 Filling the bobbin

Threading

Follow the threading guide from the instruction manual which came with the machine, or, if you have a Bernina sewing machine, use the guide in Fig. 2.37.

1 Raise presser foot and take-up lever to their highest positions.

2 Place thread reel on the pin and hold it with the right hand.

3 Pass thread with the left hand into the eyelet.

4 Draw thread into the slot of the thread tension device.

5 Hook thread into the thread regulator.

6 Draw thread into the slot of the take-up lever.

7 Pull thread down to the needle clamp eyelet.

8 Thread the needle eye from front to back and let it project about 10 cm.

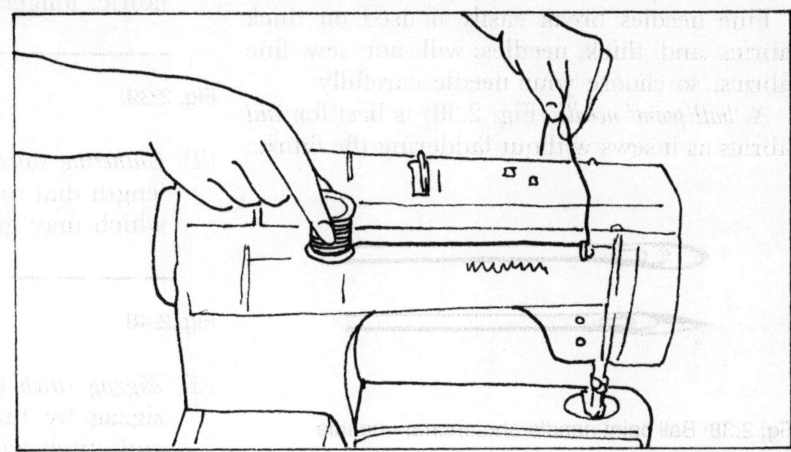

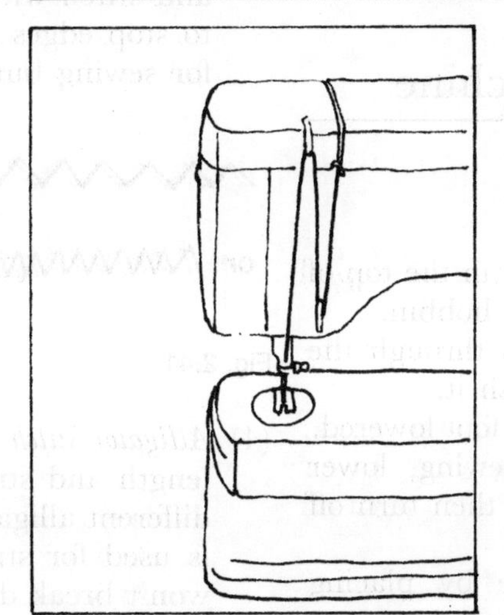

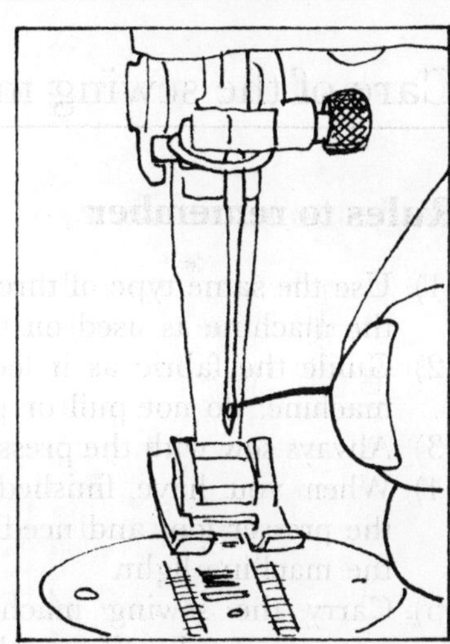

The white presser foot inset simplifies threading of the needle.

Bringing up the lower thread

1 Hold the end of the top thread loosely.

2 Turn the hand wheel towards you until the lower thread loop becomes visible in the stitch hole.

3 Pull the top thread slightly so the lower thread comes up through the stitch hole.

4 Pull the top and lower threads slightly and lay them sideways on the left under the presser foot.

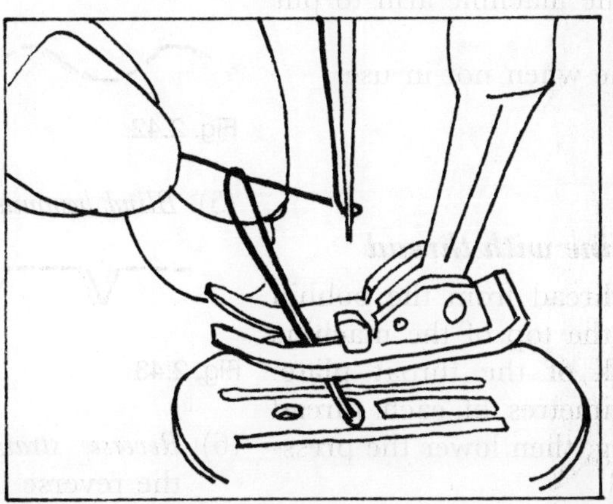

Fig. 2.37 Bernina threading guide

Changing the needle

Loosen the *needle clamp* with your fingers or a screwdriver. Remove the old or broken needle, then replace it with a new one.

Fine needles break easily if used on thick fabrics and thick needles will not sew fine fabrics, so choose your needle carefully.

A *'ball point' needle* (Fig. 2.38) is best for *knit* fabrics as it sews without laddering the fabric.

Fig. 2.38 Ball point needle and ordinary needle

Care of the sewing machine

Rules to remember

(1) Use the same type of thread in the top of the machine as used on the bobbin.
(2) Guide the fabric as it feeds through the machine, do not pull or push it.
(3) Always sew with the presser foot lowered.
(4) When you have finished sewing, lower the presser foot and needle, then turn off the machine light.
(5) Carry the sewing machine by placing your arm under the machine arm to put it away.
(6) Cover the machine when not in use.

Activity 2:2

Sewing on the machine with thread

Make sure that the thread from the bobbin and the thread from the top of the machine are both at the back of the throat plate. Leave about six centimetres of each thread before you start sewing, then lower the presser foot.

Take two pieces of scrap cotton fabric, and practice sewing the following stitches:

(1) *Straight stitch* (Fig. 2.39) Turn the stitch length dial to 2.5. Adapt the stitch length to the kind of work and the thickness of the fabric used, ie: short stitches for fine fabric, longer stitches for heavier fabric.

Fig. 2.39

(2) *Gathering stitch* (Fig. 2.40) Turn the stitch length dial to 4 to produce larger stitches which may gather the fabric.

Fig. 2.40

(3) *Zigzag stitch* (Fig. 2.41) Vary the type of zigzag by turning the stitch length dial and stitch width dial. This stitch is used to stop edges from fraying on seams and for sewing buttonholes.

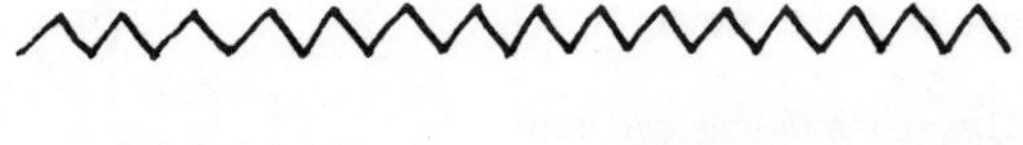

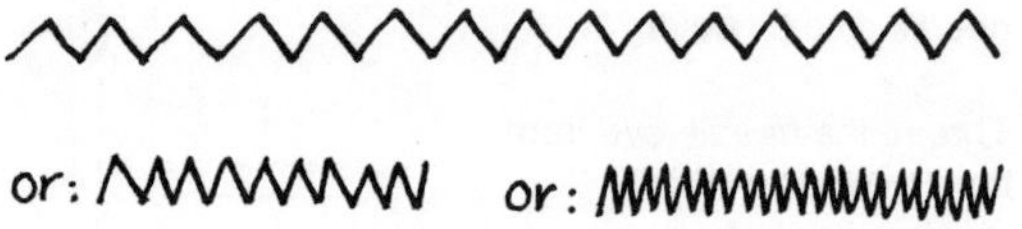

Fig. 2.41

(4) *Alligator stitch* (Fig. 2.42) Vary the stitch length and stitch width dials to produce different alligator stitch types. This stitch is used for stretch fabrics so that seams won't break during wear.

Fig. 2.42

(5) *Blind hemming stitch* (Fig. 2.43)

Fig. 2.43

(6) *Reverse straight stitch* (Fig. 2.44) Push the reverse lever or button. This stitch is used to finish off seams so that they don't come undone.

Fig. 2.44

(7) *Other fancy stitches* (Fig. 2.45) which your machine can perform.

Fig. 2.45

Now that you have mastered the basic skills of operating a sewing machine, ask your teacher to check your skills for the ***Sewing Machine Driver's Licence*** (Fig. 2.46).

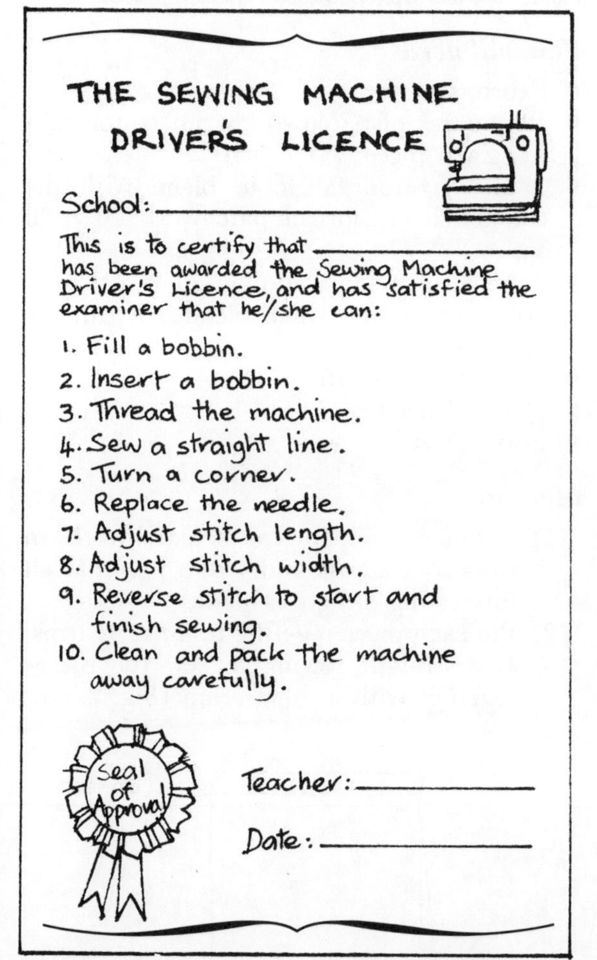
THE SEWING MACHINE DRIVER'S LICENCE

School: ____________

This is to certify that ____________ has been awarded the Sewing Machine Driver's Licence, and has satisfied the examiner that he/she can:

1. Fill a bobbin.
2. Insert a bobbin.
3. Thread the machine.
4. Sew a straight line.
5. Turn a corner.
6. Replace the needle.
7. Adjust stitch length.
8. Adjust stitch width.
9. Reverse stitch to start and finish sewing.
10. Clean and pack the machine away carefully.

Seal of Approval

Teacher: ____________

Date: ____________

Fig. 2.46 The Sewing Machine Driver's Licence

Tension

The *tension control dial* on the sewing machine should not be changed, unless it is not correct. To test if your sewing tension is correct (Fig. 2.47), see if the stitches look the same on the front and back of your straight sewing. They should link together at the centre of the two pieces of fabric as shown in this cross-sectional view.

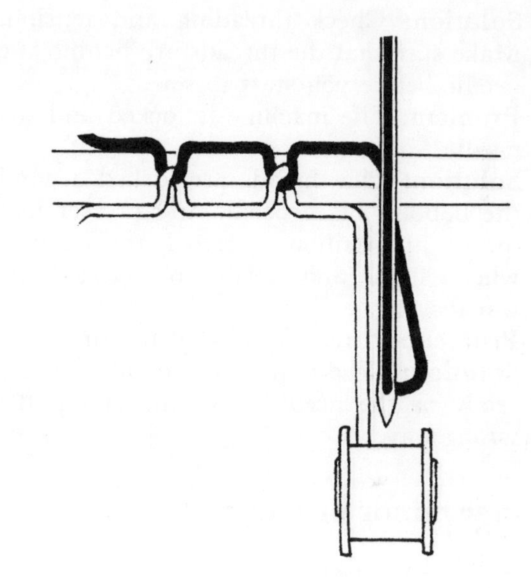

Fig. 2.47 Correct tension

Sometimes the top or bottom thread can be pulled tighter than the other, as shown in Fig. 2.48. In this case, ask your teacher to help you to adjust the tension control dial.

Fig. 2.48 (a) Needle tension too loose

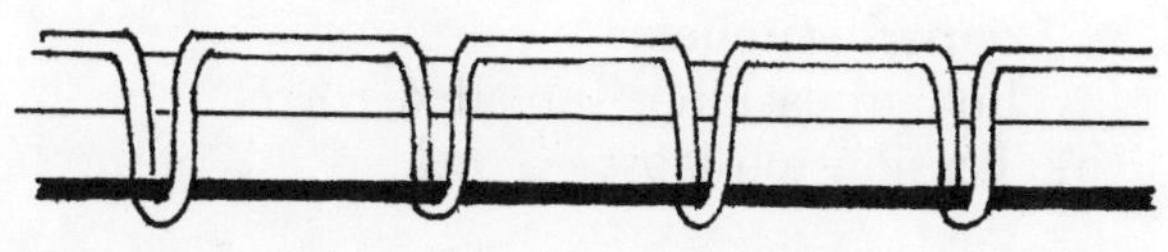

Fig. 2.48 (b) Bobbin tension too loose

Machine trouble shooting

Use the following points as a guide to try to solve your own problems with the sewing machine before asking for your teacher's assistance.

- **Problem:** As you start to stitch, the machine makes a loud noise. On the wrong side of the fabric there is a matted loop of thread.
  Solution: Check threading and tension. Make sure that the threads are behind the needle before you start to sew.
- **Problem:** The machine is locked and the needle won't move.
  Solution: The threads are locked around the bobbin. Place needle and presser foot in the up position and rock the balance wheel back and forth to release the threads.
- **Problem:** Thread breaks all the time.
  Solution: Needle may be threaded incorrectly or the needle is in the clamp the wrong way.

Other minor problems:

- **Thread breaking:**
(a) Incorrect threading
(b) Incorrect tension which needs adjustment
(c) Blunt or bent needle
(d) Broken needle
- **Fabric puckering:**
(a) Blunt needle
(b) Needle too thick
(c) Tension too tight
- **Skipped stitches:**
(a) Needle has been incorrectly inserted in the needle clamp
(b) Needle blunt or bent
(c) Needle too fine for the thread
(d) Not using a 'ball point' needle for knit fabrics
- **Looped stitches:**
(a) Bobbin case not threaded correctly
(b) Tension too loose

Activity 2:3 — Patchwork potholder

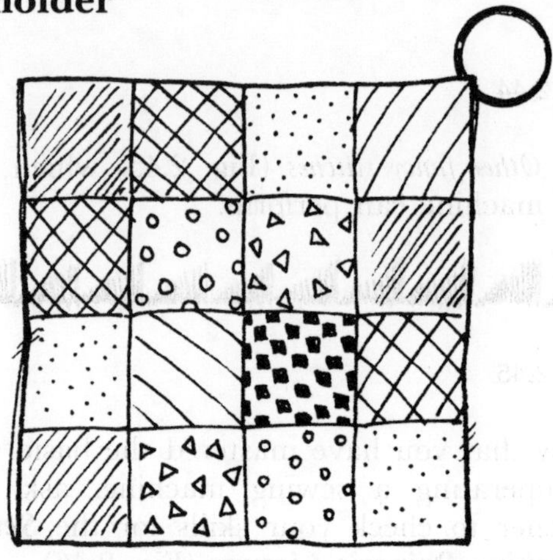

Fig. 2.49 Patchwork potholder: finished product

You will need

- Fabric scissors
- 12 squares of patchwork print cotton fabric. Each piece: 7 × 7 cm
- 1 piece cotton fabric to blend with the colours chosen for the patchwork: 20 × 20 cm
- 2 pieces of nylon wadding: 20 × 20 cm
- Polyester thread which blends in with the main fabric colours
- A 2 cm curtain ring
- 1 crewel needle
- Pins

Method

(1) Arrange each piece of patchwork in rows of 4 across and 4 down so that an interesting design is made.
(2) Pin each piece together to make 4 strips.
(3) Use straight sewing to sew the pieces together with a 1 cm seam (Fig. 2.50).

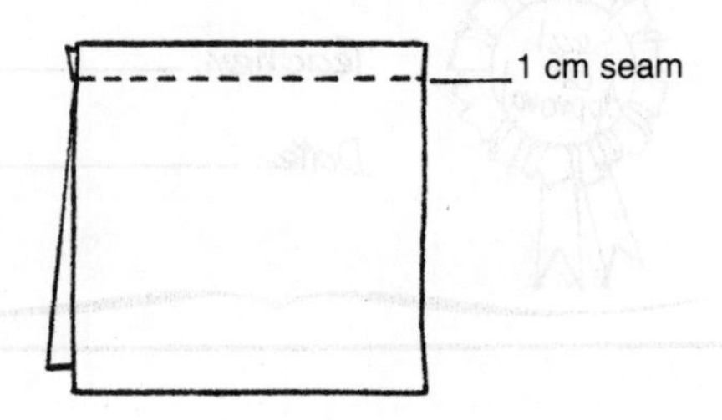

Fig. 2.50 Reverse sew to start and finish each seam

(4) Press each seam open with the iron (Fig. 2.51).

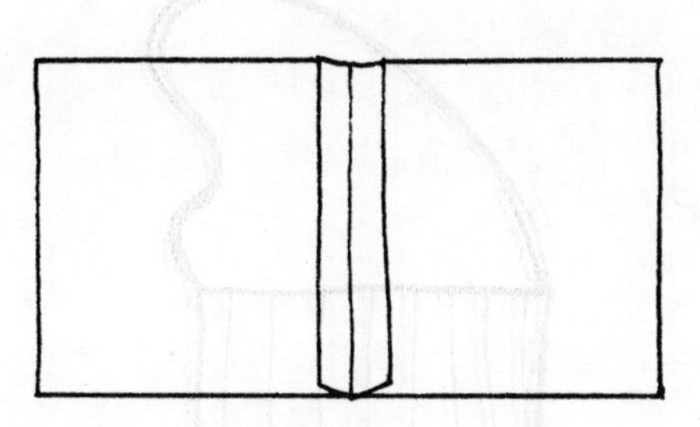

Press each seam flat after sewing

Fig. 2.51

(5) Sew the 4 strips together using a 1 cm seam to make a large square.
(6) Press seams with the iron.
(7) Place the back piece of fabric on the front of the patchwork, then the wadding on top of that.
(8) Sew straight around three and a half sides, reversing the machine at the beginning and the end of the seam (Fig. 2.52).

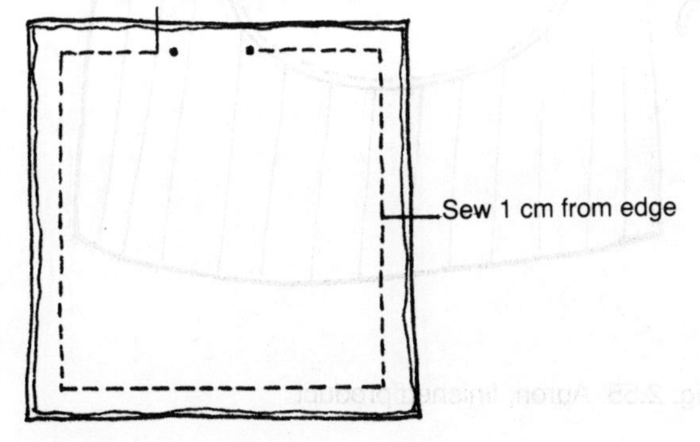

With wadding on top, sew around outside, leaving opening to pull right side through.

Fig. 2.52

(9) Turn inside out, placing a scissor point or ruler inside to make the 4 points.
(10) Fold in the top of the unsewn seam. Hand sew using a blind hemming stitch.
(11) Press lightly, then secure the curtain ring by hand sewing to one corner.

Appliqué on clothes

The word '*appliqué*' is pronounced 'applikay'. It is a way of decorating with fabrics to make motifs and designs for clothes. The easiest type of appliqué is done with *felt* because the edges don't fray.

So that the piece to be appliquéd is easy to attach, it must be strengthened with an *interfacing*. The interfacing is attached to the back of the cloth by ironing it on.

The motif you make can be appliquéd on to the piece of clothing by hand blanket stitching, or by using the buttonhole stitch on the sewing machine. The appliqué may need some dressing up with *embroidery* to give it character, particularly animal motifs where eyes and lines create the features.

Activity 2:4 — Appliqué

Try some simple appliqué by choosing a design and tracing it out on fabric with marking chalk. The designs in Fig. 2.53 may give you some ideas.

Fig. 2.53 Appliqué designs

You will need

- Fabric scissors
- Pins
- A small piece of iron-on interfacing
- Thread to match the appliquéd fabric
- Another piece of fabric to sew the motif on
- Marking chalk

Method

(1) Cut a piece of interfacing about the same size as your chosen design. Iron it on to the back of the fabric.
(2) Cut out the design from the front, through the interfacing.
(3) Pin the motif onto the piece of clothing or sample.
(4) Tack around it using a large stitch to hold it in place. Press well.
(5) Sew carefully around the motif using the buttonhole stitch on the machine. Press well.

Fig. 2.54 Appliqué sample

Activity 2.5 — Apron

Fig. 2.55 Apron, finished product

You will need

- Fabric scissors
- 1 m of fabric
- Cotton tape for straps
- Polyester thread to match the fabric
- Pins
- Tapemeasure
- Marking chalk
- Scrap fabrics for appliqué decoration
- Iron-on interfacing large enough to fit your motif.

Method

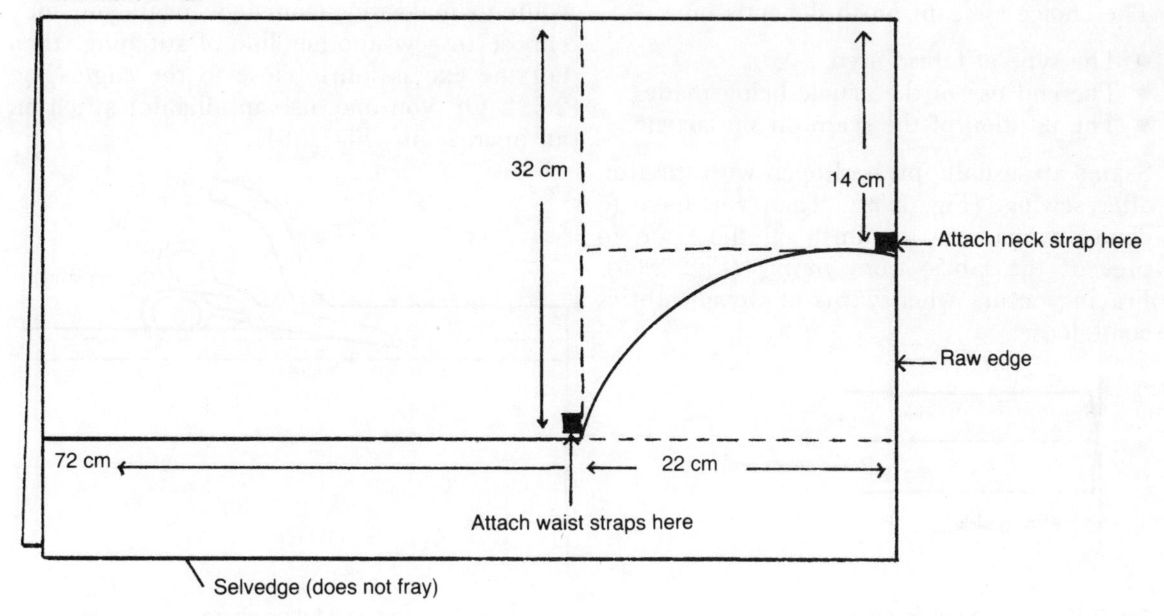

Fig. 2.56 Cutting out method

(1) Follow the guide for marking out the pattern. Use marking chalk for the outline and a ruler for the straight lines. Check with your teacher before cutting out.
(2) Cut straps from cotton tape: 2 straps 65 cm long and 1 strap for the neck, 45 cm long.
(3) Use the pattern for the tomato appliqué pocket or your own design. Use the method for appliquéing in the previous activity.
(4) Pin the pocket onto the apron, tack and then buttonhole stitch, leaving enough room for your hand at the top. Press well.
(5) Turn over 1 cm hems at the side curves of the apron (Fig. 2.57). Iron flat, then pin and sew using the straight sewing stitch. Press well.
(6) Turn over top and sides of the apron. Sew with the straight sewing stitch. Press well.
(7) Turn over a 2 cm hem at the bottom. Sew using the straight sewing stitch. Press well.
(8) Attach tapes using the process shown in Fig. 2.58.

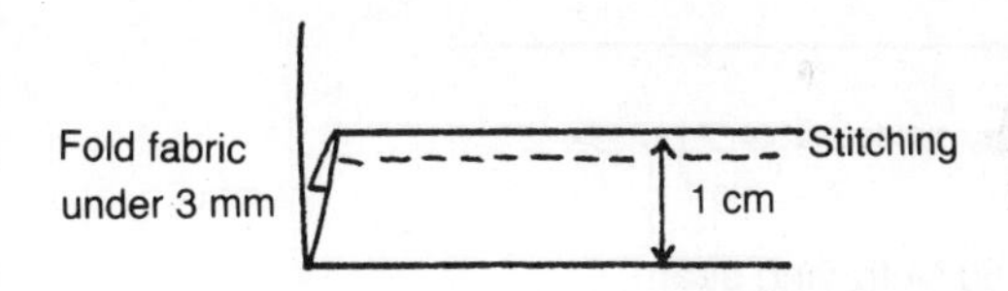

*Press flat with the iron before sewing the seam, and after it is sewn.

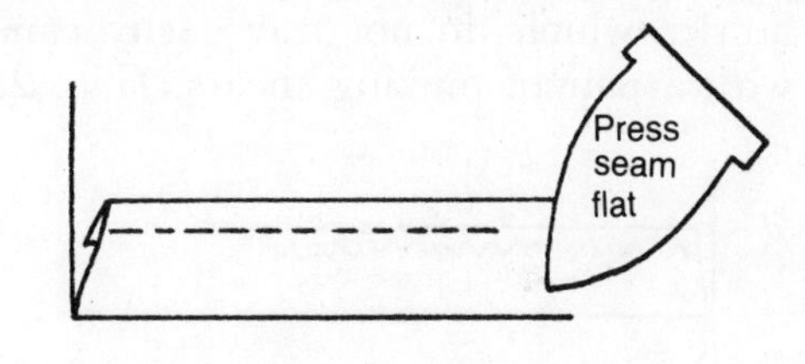

Fig. 2.57

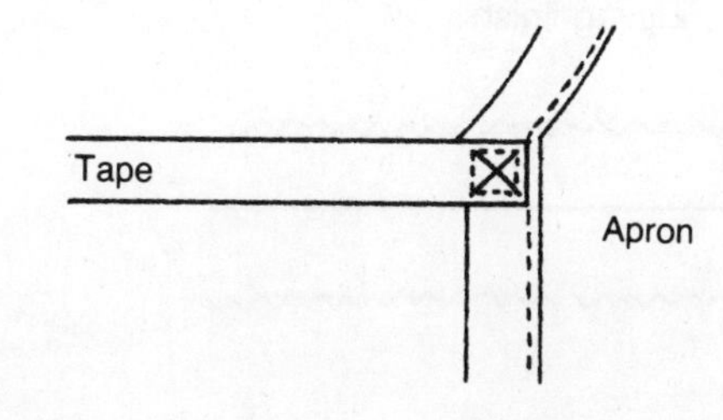

Fig. 2.58

Seam finishes

The choice of seam finish depends on:

- The type of fabric used.
- The end use of the article being made.
- The position of the seam on the article.

Seams are usually pressed open with the iron after sewing. (Fig. 2.59). Then you have to choose which way to finish off the seam to prevent the fabric from *fraying* (Fig. 2.60). Fraying occurs when yarns of woven fabrics come loose.

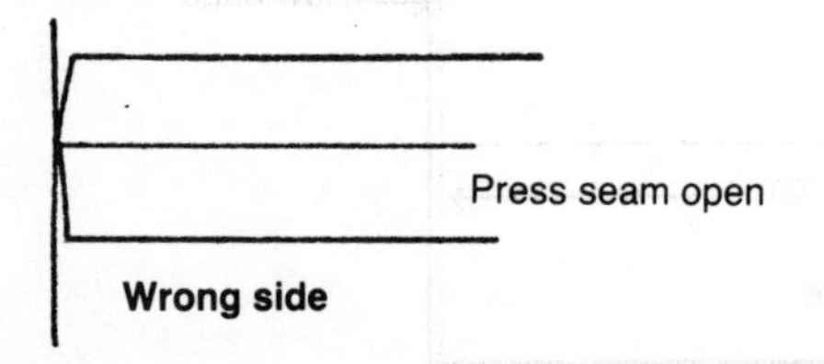

Fig. 2.59 Seam pressed open

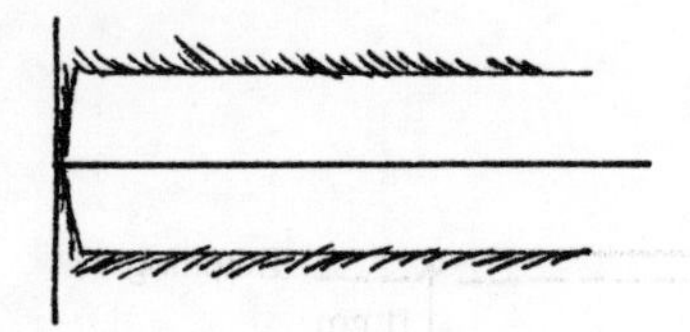

Fig. 2.60 A fraying seam

Most seams can be zigzagged on the raw edges to prevent fraying (Fig. 2.61). Thick fabrics which do not fray easily can be cut with a pair of pinking shears. (Fig. 2.62).

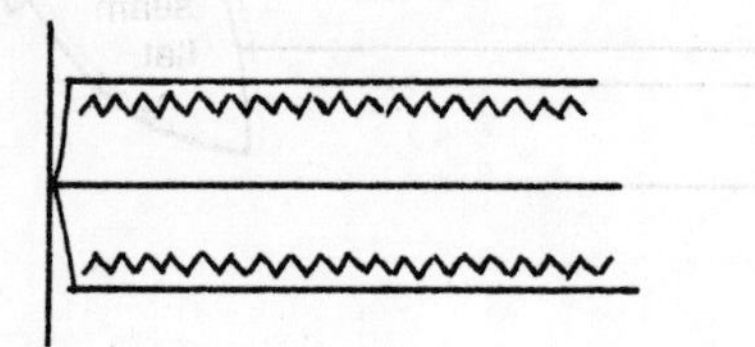

Fig. 2.61 Zigzag finish

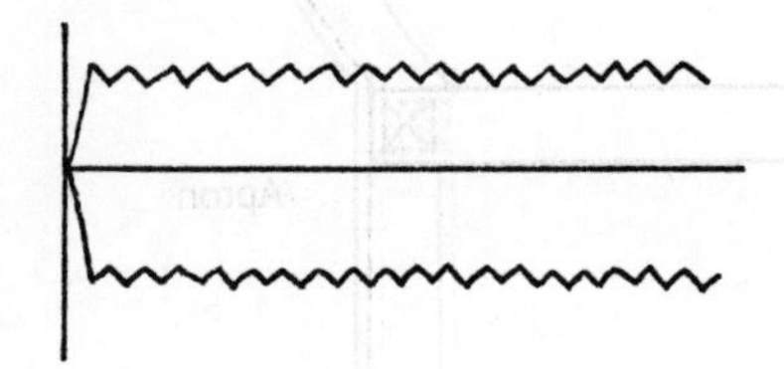

Fig. 2.62 Pinked finish

Seams on knit fabrics don't have to be finished as knits do not fray easily. If you want to make the seam look neat, you may choose to sew another line of stitching, then cut the excess fabric close to the edge (Fig. 2.63). Or, you may use an alligator stitch on an open seam (Fig. 2.64).

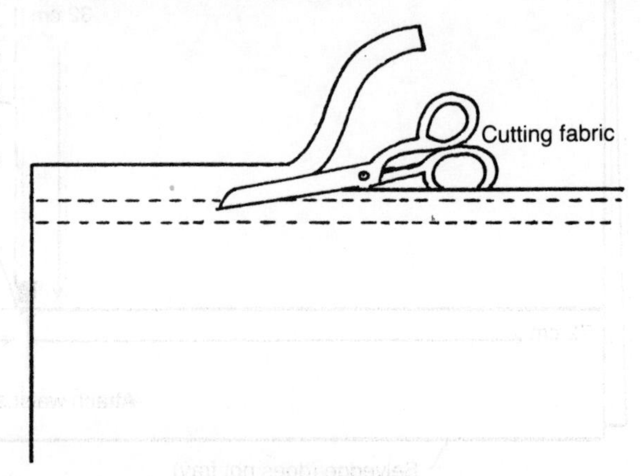

Fig. 2.63 Cutting a knit fabric seam

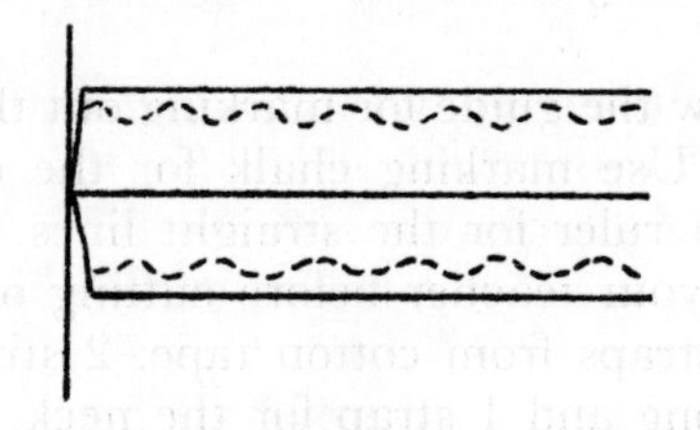

Fig. 2.64 Alligator stitch

Activity 2:6 — Shorts

The shorts in Fig. 2.65 will fit a 12–13 year old boy or girl.

You will need

- 1 m of 90 cm wide fabric such as cotton drill or gaberdine. Use soft, light nylon or polyester for running shorts
- Thread to match
- 70 cm of 1.5 cm wide elastic

Method

(1) Cut the shorts out using the pattern in Fig. 2.66.

Fig. 2.65 The finished shorts

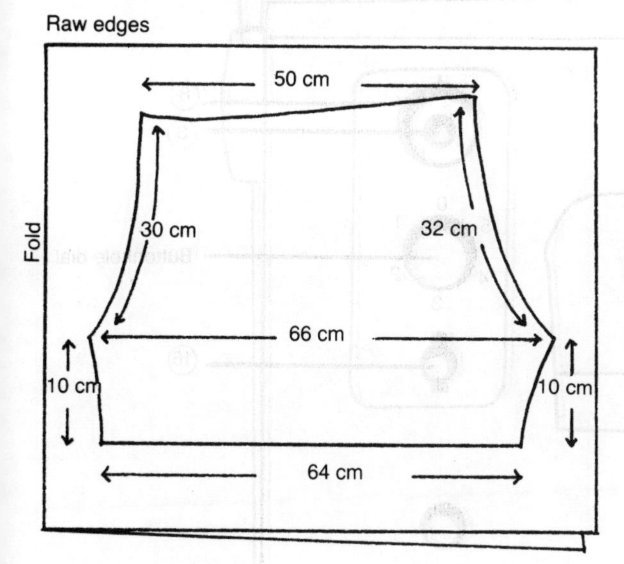

Fig. 2.66 Cutting layout

(2) Pin front and back seams. Machine stitch, remembering to reverse at the end of each seam. Press open and finish by zigzagging. Cut the seam carefully at the curve to allow it to lie flat (Fig. 2.67).

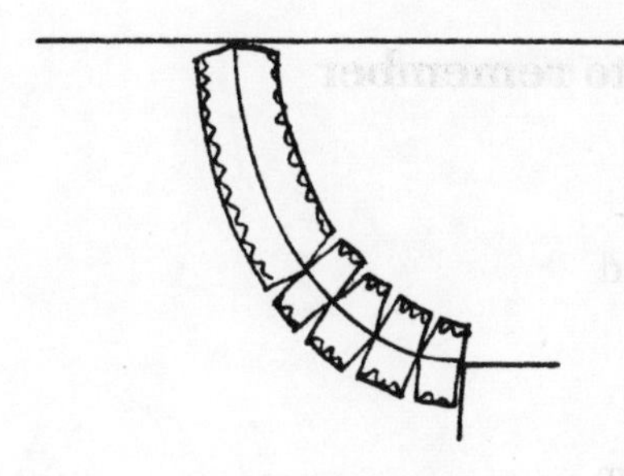

Fig. 2.67 Cutting the seam to allow it to lie flat

(3) Zigzag the top edge and turn over the top 3 cm. Press flat. Sew the elastic casing 2 cm from the top edge. Leave a space of 2 cm to allow the elastic to be threaded through.

(4) Sew the bottom seams together. Press open and zigzag finish.

(5) Turn the leg hems under 1 cm (Fig. 2.68), then sew with straight machine stitching. Press flat before sewing. Make sure they are well pinned.

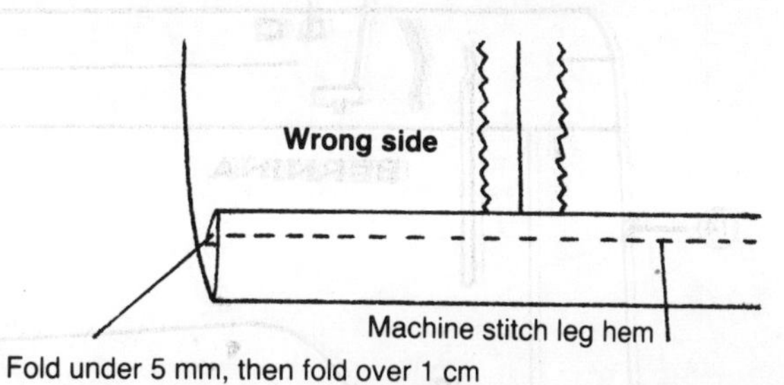

Fig. 2.68 Turning under the leg hems

(6) Feed elastic through the casing using a safety pin attached to the elastic. Try the shorts on and fit the elastic to make it comfortable around the waist. Pin the elastic ends together and sew them by hand. (Fig. 2.69).

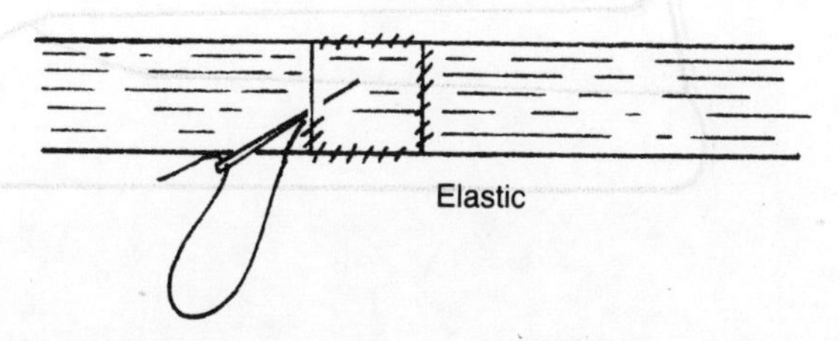

Fig. 2.69 Sewing the elastic ends together

Words to remember

bodkin
tapestry
mercerised
polyester
woollen
macramé
Inkle loom
8-shaft loom
drop spindle
crochet
presser foot
throat plate
bobbin case
needle clamp
alligator stitch
blind hemming
tension
appliqué
felt
interfacing
embroidery
buttonhole
fray

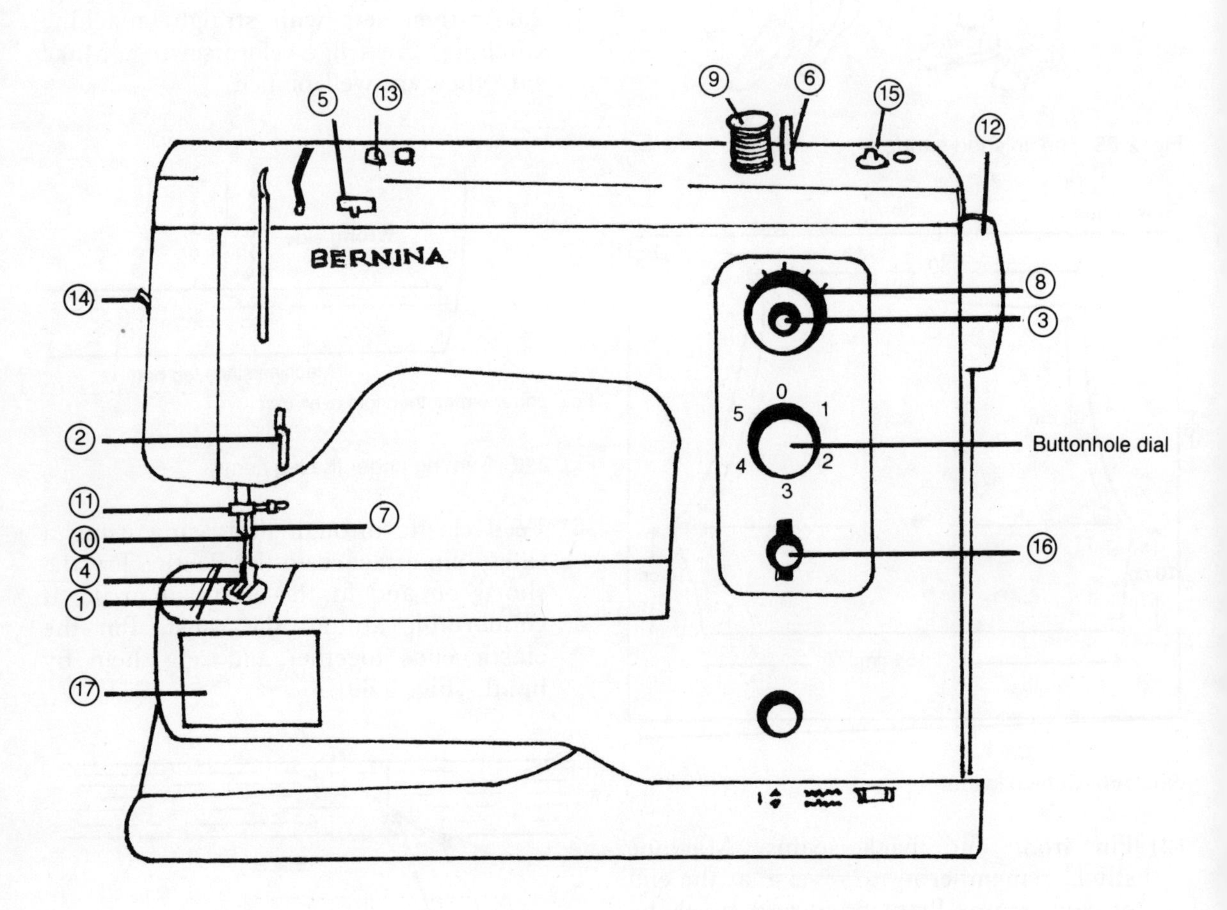

Fig. 2.70

Activity 2:7 — Revision

(1) Complete the word chart in Fig. 2.70 to name parts of the sewing machine.

(2) Fill in the missing words to complete the sentences:

(a) Embroidery scissors have fine, _ _ _ _ _ points. [5 letters]

(b) _ _ _ _ _ _ _ shears are used to cut fabrics which do not fray easily. [7 letters]

(c) All fabric markers wash out with water and _ _ _ _ _ _ _ _ _. [9 letters]

(d) An example of a synthetic thread is _ _ _ _ _ _ _ _ _. [9 letters]

(e) _ _ _ _ _ _ _ _ _ _ _ _ is one of the oldest types of hand spinning. [2 words, 4 letters, 8 letters]

(3) Can you unscramble the coded message in Fig. 2.71?

CODE

abc	def	ghi
jkl	mno	pqr
stu	vwx	yz

Fig. 2.71

Further reading

Butterick Sewing Book

NSW Department of Education Curriculum Ideas:
Textiles and Design—Introductory Programs, 1980
Spinning—An Australian Craft, 1982
Schlencker Waddell, J. *Introducing Home Economics*, Macmillan, Melbourne, 1984
Vulker, J. and Cooper, H. *Textiles, Fabric & Design*, Macmillan, Melbourne, 1985

3

Textile manufacture

Three important terms

To be a wise textile consumer, it is important that you know the difference between a fibre, yarn, and fabric.

A ***fibre*** (Fig. 3.1) is the basic material used in the production of a yarn. A ***yarn*** (Fig. 3.2) is made by twisting fibres together to form a strand. A ***fabric*** (Fig. 3.3) is often referred to as a material.

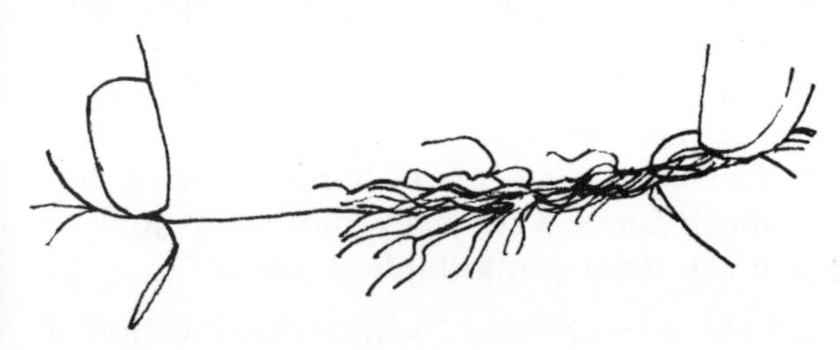

Fig. 3.1 Fibre

Fig. 3.2 Yarn

Fig. 3.3 Fabric

Making fabric from fibre

- by ***bonding fibres:***

For example, *felt* is made by shrinking woollen fibres or acrylic fibres together. *Vilene* stiffening for collars and cuffs is made from cotton fibres and glue. *Dishcloths* (Fig. 3.4) are matted together, then heat-set into shape.

Fig. 3.4 Dishcloths, felt hat, and vilene

- by ***twisting fibres:***

Fibres are twisted into yarns which in turn can be made into fabrics by weaving, crocheting, knitting and knotting (macramé).

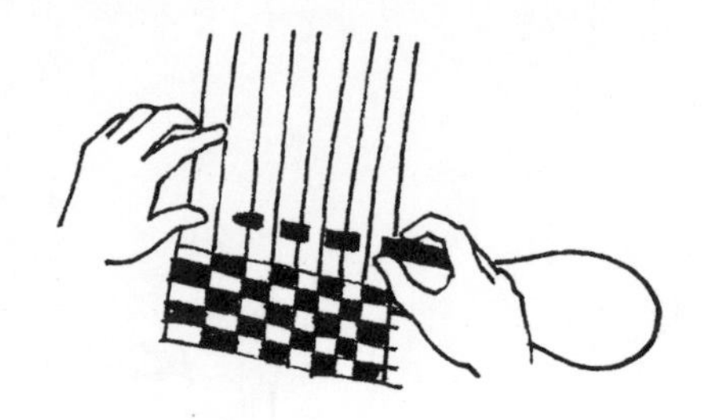

Fig. 3.5 Weaving

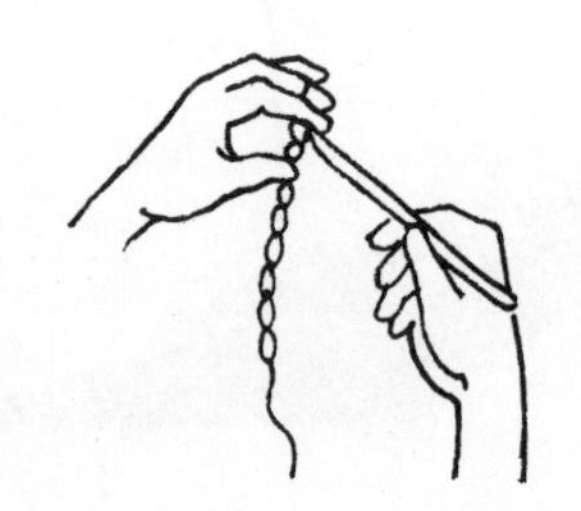

Fig. 3.6 Crocheting

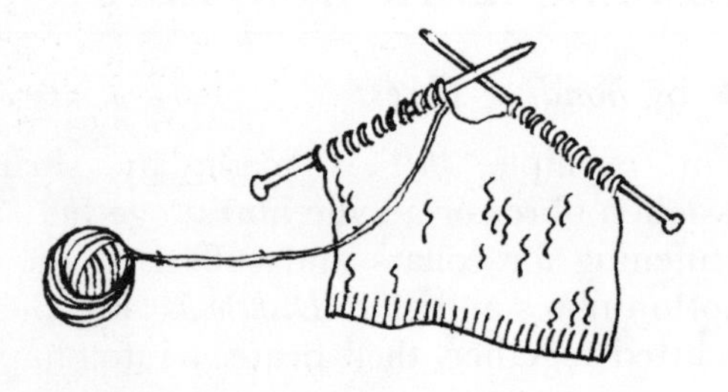

Fig. 3.7 Knitting

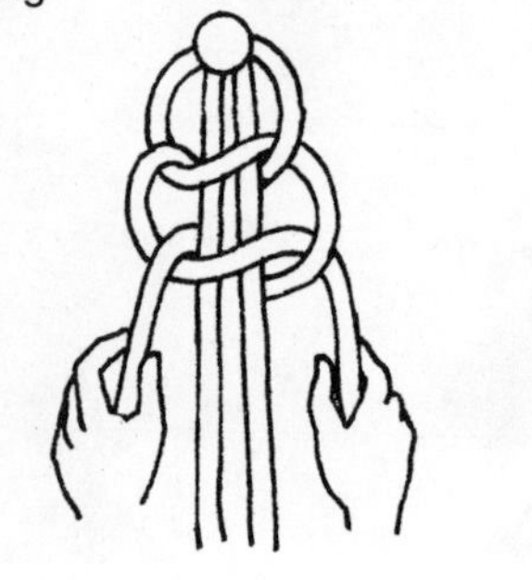

Fig. 3.8 Macramé

Activity 3:1

(1) Collect fibre, yarn and fabric samples for your workbook. Paste in and label them.
(2) Collect samples of different types of fabrics to paste in your workbook. Cut with pinking shears to make them neat and prevent fraying. Ask your teacher to help you name the fabrics, then write the names under each sample in your workbook.
(3) Under each sample, write down the uses each fabric may have. For example, a two-way stretch fabric may be suitable for a track suit or surfboard cover.

Types of fibres

For a fibre to be useful for making into fabric, it must have the following properties:

- *Strength* — to withstand wear and laundering.
- *Cohesion* — to allow fibres to be spun into yarns.
- *Length* — to allow fibres to be aligned in the same direction for spinning.
- *Flexibility* — to allow fibres to bend and move easily with body movement and to make them comfortable to wear.

All fibres can fit into a simple classification of *natural* or *manufactured* fibres.

Natural fibres

Animal	**Vegetable**	**Mineral**
cotton	wool	asbestos
flax (linen)	silk	

Manufactured fibres

Cellulosic	**Synthetic**	**Inorganic**
rayon	polyester	glass
	nylon	metal
	acrylic	
	Spandex (Lycra)	

Activity 3:2

(1) What types of fibres are used to make house roof insulation?
(2) How are these fibres made into a fabric?
(3) Fill in the following chart in your workbook. (There may be more than one answer for each space.) When you have finished ask your teacher to check your answers.

Fibre	Method of fabric production	Fabric name
wool	bonding	felt
nylon		nylon wadding
	weaving	denim
flax	weaving	
	knitting	rib knit
flax		rope
cotton		calico
polyester		single knit
silk	tying	

Bonding fibres together

There are many more textiles made from *bonded* fabric today than ever before. The main reason is that they are quick and easy to produce. The fibres are matted, glued or stitched together. They don't have to be spun into yarns and then woven or knitted into fabric. This saves time and money in production and so these fabrics are cheaper than others.

Disposable nappies, dishcloths, disposable underwear, and even tablecloths are now made from bonded fabrics (Fig. 3.9a). It is now possible to supply all the requirements for a baby from bonded fabrics, including gowns, bibs, nappies (Fig. 3.9b), sheets and pillow cases. When they are soiled or outgrown, they can be thrown away.

Fig. 3.9 Disposable bonded textiles

Fig. 3.10 'I'll bet they feel cold this morning!'

Activity 3:3 — Making woollen felt

You will need

- Some combed wool fibres
- 1 litre of boiling water
- Metal spoon or glass stirring rod
- Large beaker or bowl

Method

(1) Place half of the combed wool fibres into the boiling water. Save the other half as a control so that you can compare the differences in the fibres after felting.
(2) Stir for 5 minutes.
(3) Remove the fibres, squeeze out the water, and dry the fibres.
(4) Compare the fibre mat with the control combed fibres.
(5) Place a sample of your felt and the control fibres in your workbook.
(6) **Answer the following questions in your workbook**
  (a) Look closely at one of the felted wool fibres. What is the difference between the control fibres and the matted ones?
  (b) Look at both fibres under the microscope. Sketch your fibres. What are the main differences?
  (c) How do you think synthetic *acrylic* felt is made?

Activity 3:4 — Elephant eggcosies

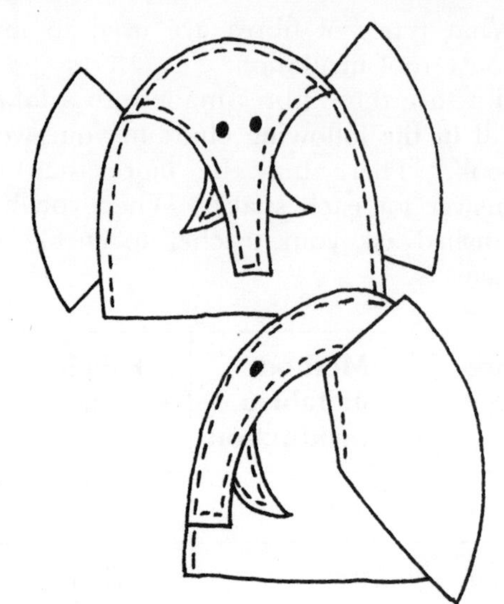
Fig. 3.11 Eggcosy

You will need

- Grey felt for the body and ears
- Pink felt for the trunk
- White felt for the tusks
- Black felt for the eyes (or you could use a fabric painting pen)
- Grey polyester thread

Method

(1) Copy the pattern pieces for the elephant onto tracing paper (Fig. 3.12).

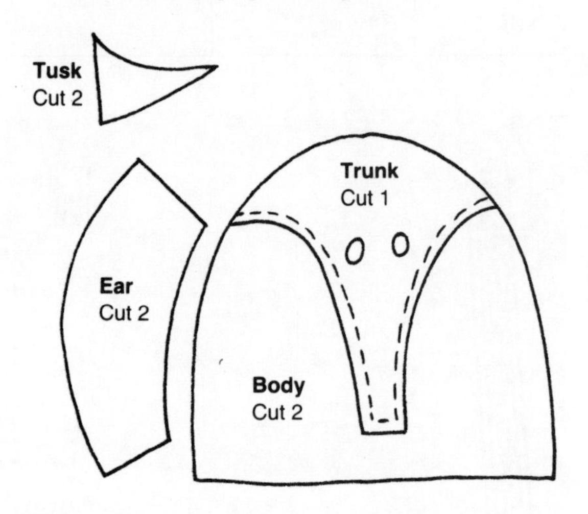

Fig. 3.12 Pattern pieces for the elephant

(2) Pin the patterns to the felt and cut out carefully.
(3) Pin the tusks under the trunk, then pin the trunk onto the front body piece.
(4) Hand stitch or machine stitch the tusks and trunk in place. You may want to have the elephant trunk turned up at the end. If so, then only sew to the end of the tusks (Fig. 3.13).

Fig. 3.13 Finished cosy with trunk turned up

(5) Place the ears on either side of the front piece, then pin it to the back piece.
(6) Stitch around the outside (Fig. 3.4).

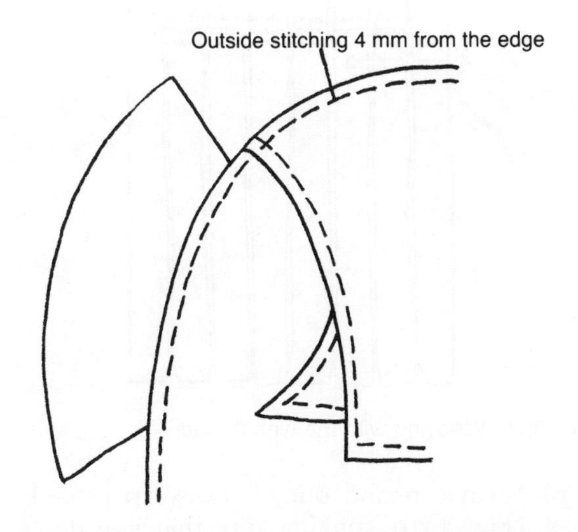

Fig. 3.14 Stitching around the outside of the elephant

(7) Hand stitch the eyes or use a pen to draw them.

Weaving fabrics

Weaving is a way of making fabric by crossing threads under and over each other. The *warp* threads go up and down (vertically), and the *weft* threads fill in the warp when you weave them across, as shown in Fig. 3.15.

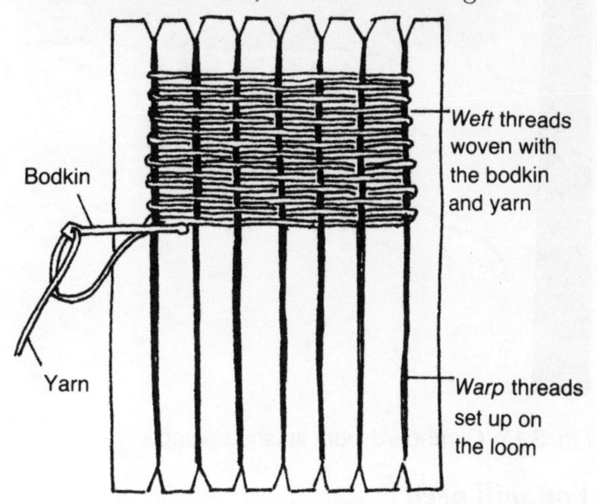

Fig. 3.15 Weaving showing warp and weft threads

Weaving is done on a *loom*. There are many different types of looms, a simple one is a cardboard loom. The cardboard loom, illustrated in Fig. 3.16 allows you to weave simple patterns easily.

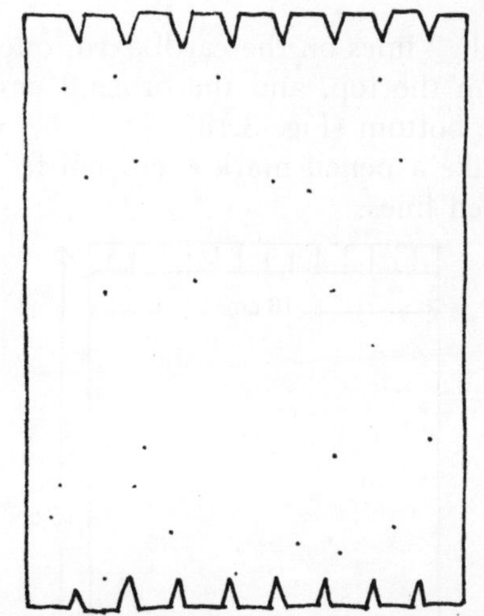

Fig. 3.16 Cardboard loom

Activity 3:5 — Weaving on a cardboard loom

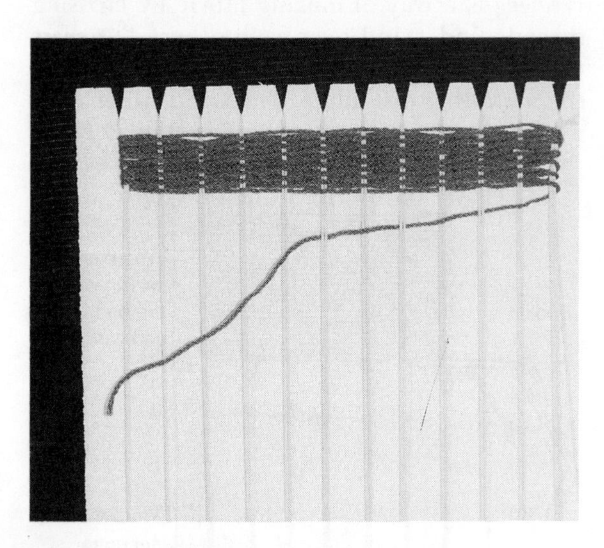

Fig. 3.17 Cardboard loom finished sample

You will need

- A strong piece of cardboard 10 cm × 15 cm
- Strong cotton thread for the warp
- 8 or 12-ply wool knitting or carpet yarn for the weft
- Scissors
- A ruler and a pencil
- Bodkin needle

Method

(1) Rule 2 lines on the cardboard, one 2 cm from the top, and the other 2 cm from the bottom (Fig. 3.18).

(2) Make a pencil mark every cm from the ruled lines.

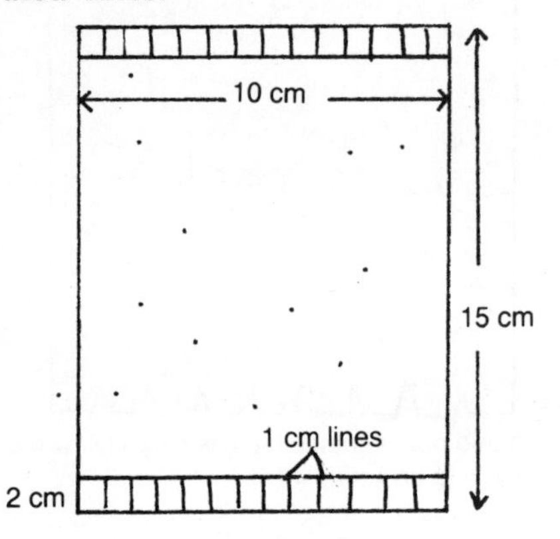

Fig. 3.18 Ruling up the cardboard loom

(3) Rule lines from these marks to the edge of your cardboard, then cut each to the 2 cm line.

(4) Take the warp yarn around the cardboard tabs, tying it off at each end.

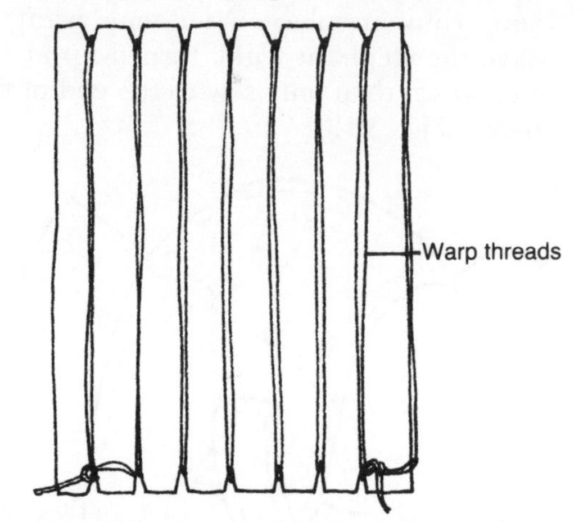

Fig. 3.19 Threading the warp

(5) Now you are ready to start weaving with the weft thread. Thread 50 cm of yarn onto a bodkin needle. Tie the end of this thread to the first warp thread, on the right-hand side of your loom (Fig 3.19).

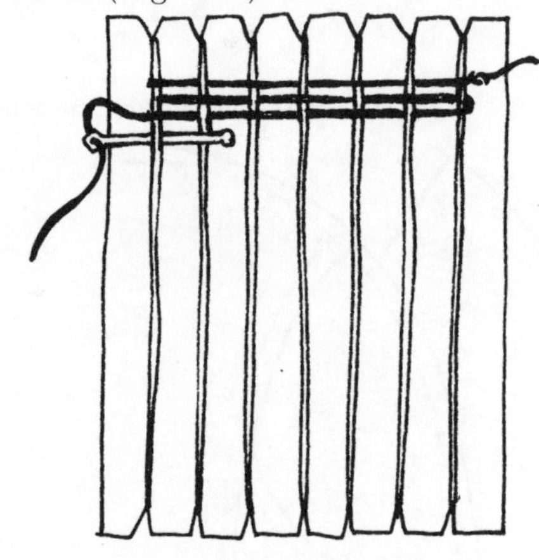

Fig. 3.20 Weaving with the weft thread

(6) Weave in and out of the warp threads (Fig. 3.20), making sure that you don't pull the weft tight at each end or the weaving will curl in. After each row, push the weft up tightly using a ruler (Fig. 3.21).

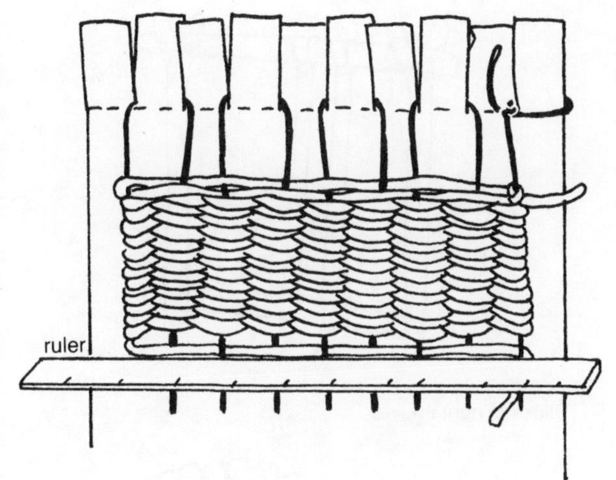

Fig. 3.21 Pushing the weft threads together

(7) The 2nd row is the opposite to the 1st. Where you went under in the 1st, go over on the 2nd row.
(8) The 3rd, 5th, 7th, etc. rows are the same as the 1st row. The 4th, 6th, 8th, etc. rows are the same as the 2nd row.
(9) When you want to change the weft colour, or you have finished the thread, weave the weft to the centre of a row. Cut the thread, then start the next row 3 warp threads back (Fig. 3.22).

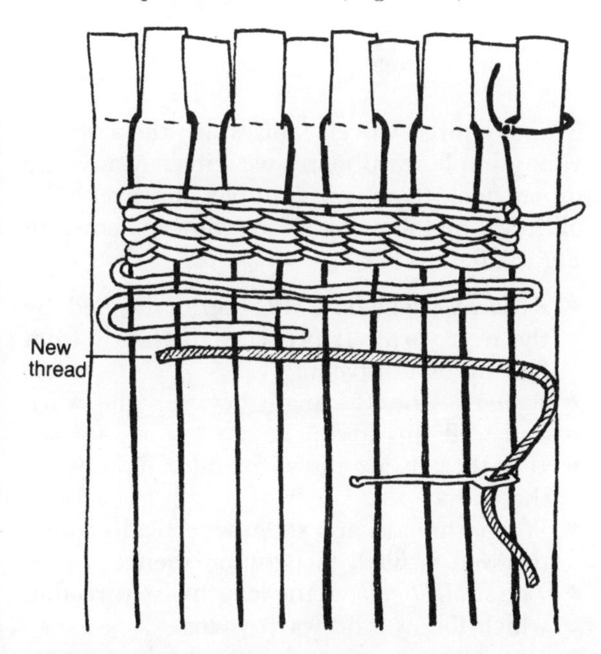

Fig. 3.22 Starting a new weft yarn

(10) When you have finished weaving, cut and tie the warp yarns as shown in Fig. 3.23. You may use your weaving as a sample for your workbook or make a purse, mat or wall hanging from it. Try cardboard weaving, by inventing your own weave patterns and colour combinations.

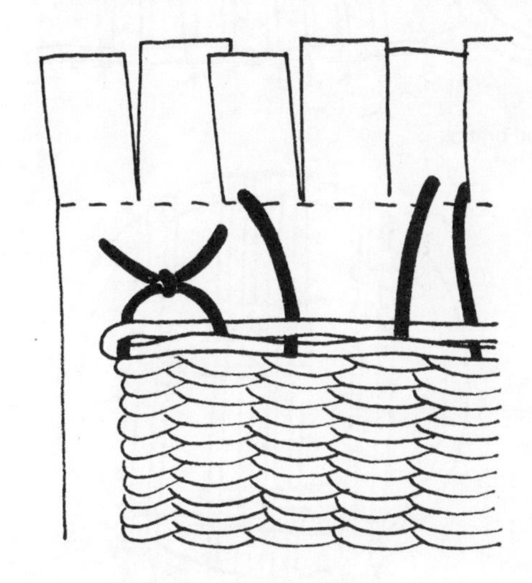

Fig. 3.23 Tying off the warp ends

(11) **Answer the following questions in your workbook**
(a) Why is it important to have a strong, firm *warp* yarn?
(b) In this activity you were using a plain weave. Find out the names of other types of weaves and sketch them on graph paper.
(c) Draw a design for a cardboard weaving for a wall hanging for your room. Label or colour in the colours and weaves used.
(d) What would happen if you made your warp threads closer together on the cardboard loom?

Activity 3:6 — Extension

Try weaving on a forked branch of a tree, a round cardboard loom, metal rings or tied twigs as shown in Fig. 3.24.

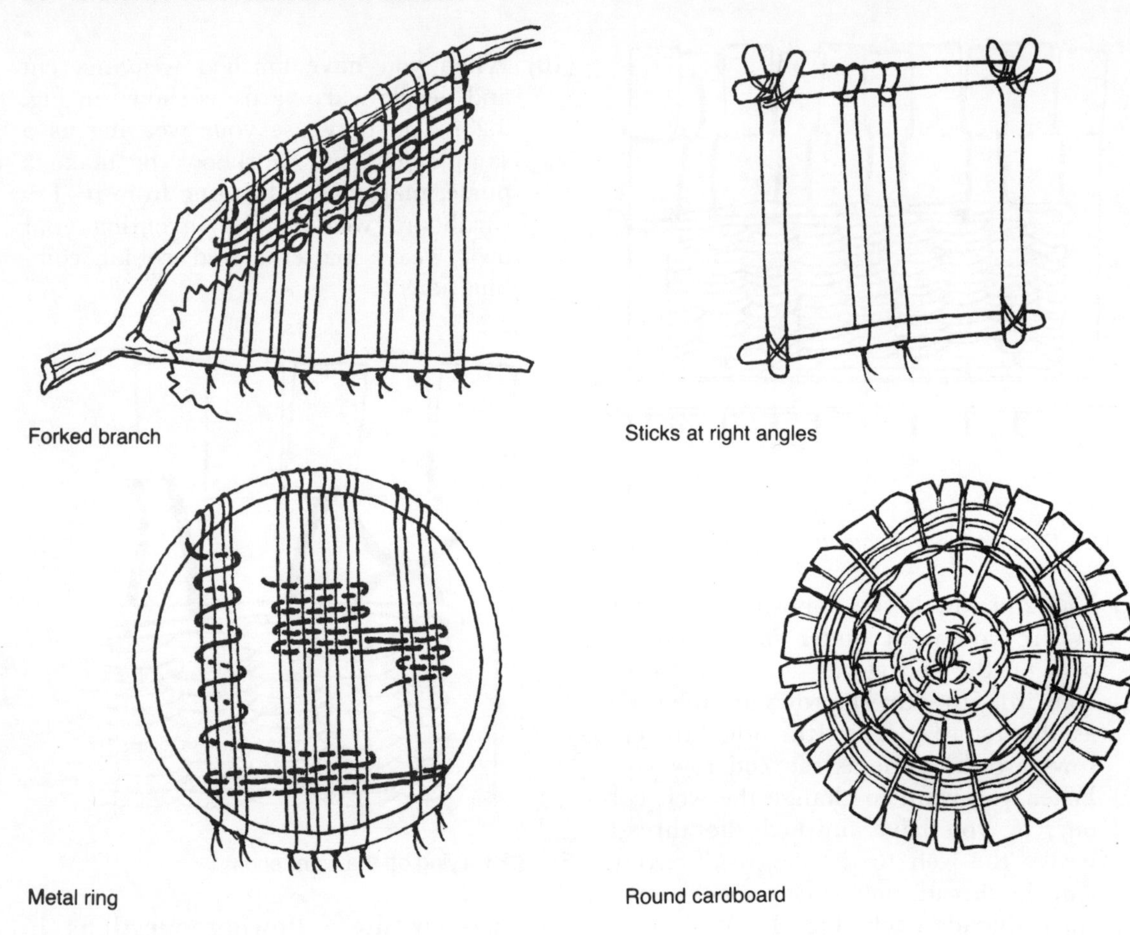

Fig. 3.24 Other types of looms to try

Let's look at some manufactured woven fabric

Fig. 3.25 Woven fabrics on rolls in a shop

Manufactured woven fabrics are the same as your simple cardboard weaving. Many are much finer than your sample, however they all have the following in common as shown in Fig. 3.26:

- *A selvedge* which is the border formed by the weft yarns. It prevents the fabric from fraying or unravelling.
- *A bias* is the 45° angle between the warp and weft threads.
- *Weft* threads are the yarns filled in between the warp.
- Warp threads are set up vertically, then the weft is filled in between them.
- The *straight grain* is the lengthwise direction which follows the warp yarns.
- *Raw edges* are on each end of fabric where the length is cut off the loom.

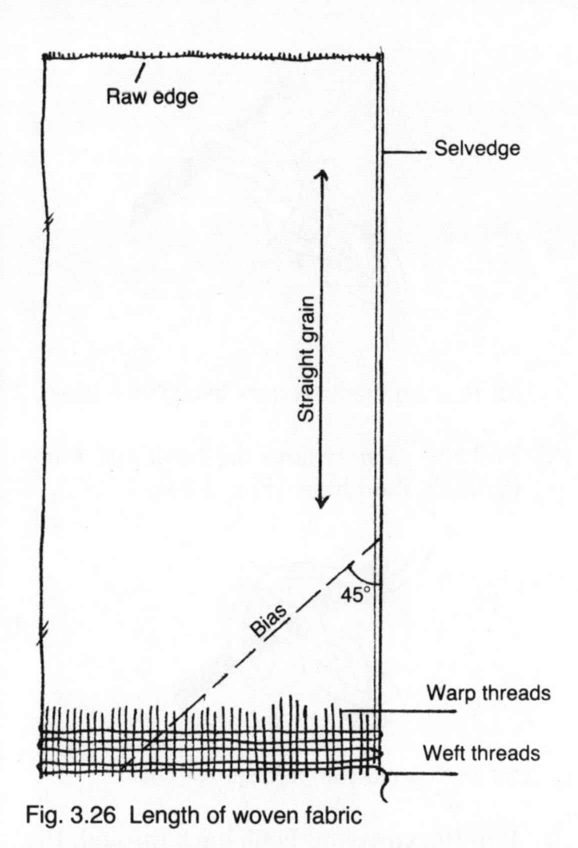

Fig. 3.26 Length of woven fabric

Activity 3:7 — Examining woven fabric closely

You will need

- A fabric sample with a selvedge
- Glue

Method

(1) Pull gently along the straight grain of the fabric to unravel some of the warp threads, opposite the selvedge.
(2) Pull gently at some of the weft threads to unravel them.
(3) See the bias stretch by pulling at a 45° angle across the fabric.
(4) Glue the sample into your workbook.
(5) Label the following parts of your sample by drawing an arrow to the parts:

- selvedge
- raw edge
- bias
- weft threads
- warp threads
- straight grain

Crocheting

Crochet is a way of making a single yarn into fabric by looping it. The word *crochet* comes from a French word meaning 'hook'.

Crocheting is a craft rather than a method of producing fabric on a large scale for the manufacturing industry.

Activity 3:8 — Learning to crochet

You will need

- Metal crochet hook (size 5 mm)
- 8-ply woollen knitting yarn

Method

(1) Hold the crochet hook like a pencil (Fig. 3.27).

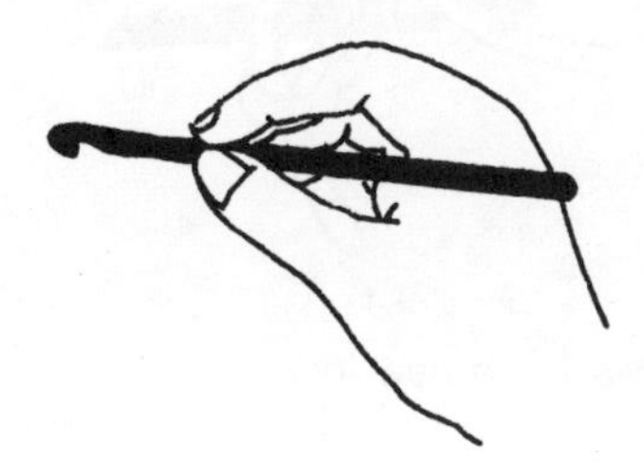

Fig. 3.27 Holding the crochet hook

(2) Make a circle and pull the long end of the wool through it (Fig. 3.28).

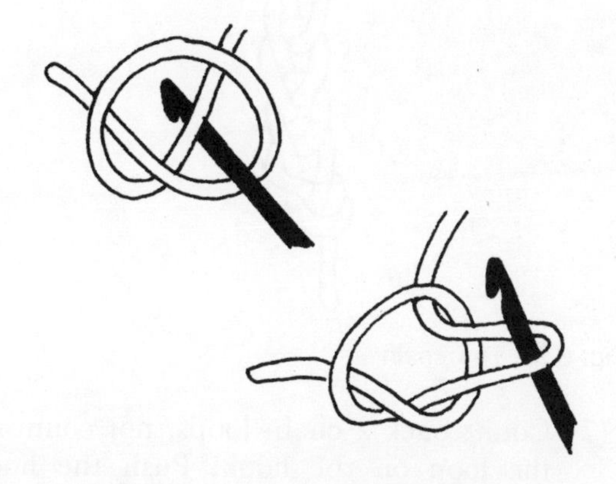

Fig. 3.28 Pulling the yarn through the circle

(3) Pull both ends of the wool to tighten the knot.

(4) Pull the loop though and hook the wool over the crochet hook (fig. 3.29).

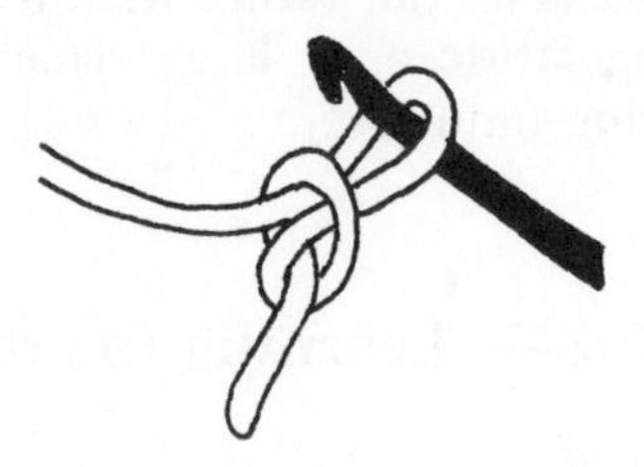

Fig. 3.29 Making a loop

(5) Pull the loop through so that you have made a new loop (Fig. 3.30).

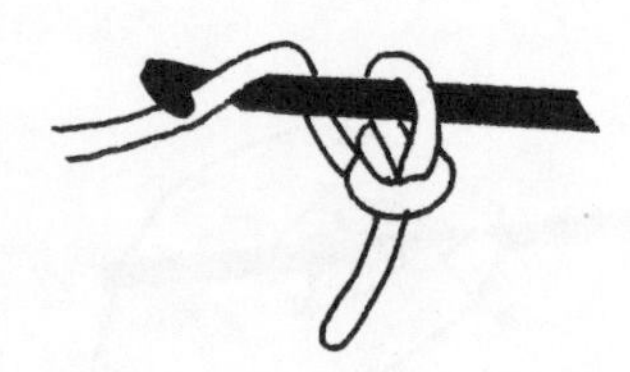

Fig. 3.30 Making a new loop

(6) Keep pulling through new loops until you have made a long chain (Fig. 3.31).

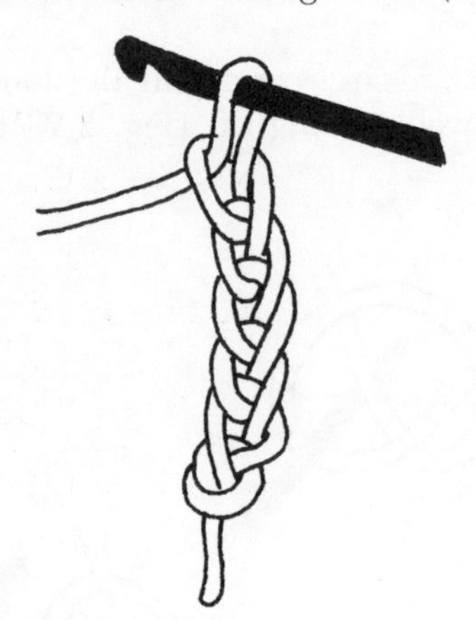

Fig. 3.31 The chain

(7) Count back 2 chain loops, not counting the loop on the hook. Push the hook under the top 2 loops of the chain (Fig. 3.32).

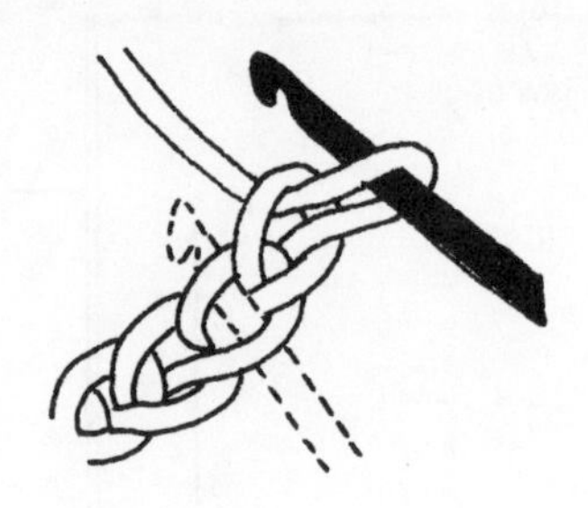

Fig. 3.32 Pushing the hook back through the chain

(8) Pull the yarn around the hook and back through the chain (Fig. 3.33).

Fig. 3.33 Pulling the yarn through the chain

(9) Pull the yarn and hook back through the chain so that there are 2 loops on the hook (Fig. 3.34).

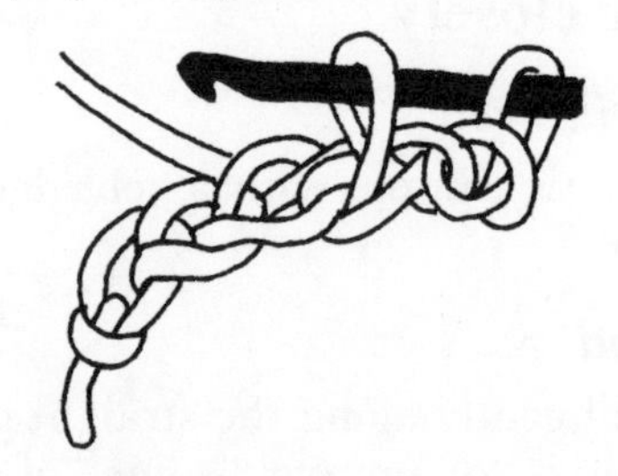

Fig. 3.34 Two loops on the chain

(10) Hook the yarn and pull it back through the 2 loops (Fig. 3.35). You now have 1 loop on the hook.

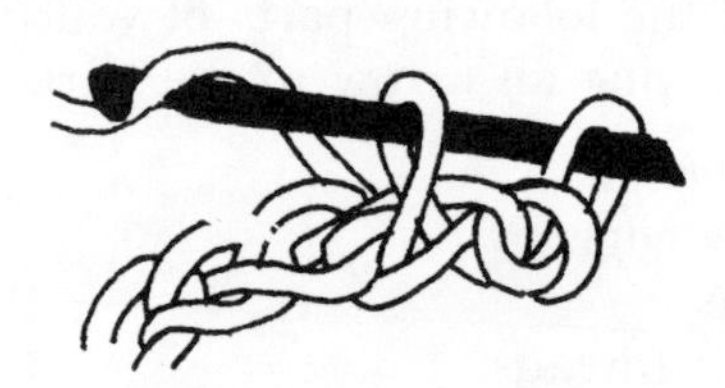

Fig. 3.35 Pulling the yarn through the 2 loops

(11) Keep crocheting to the end of the chain. Make a single chain at the end of the row. Turn your crocheting around and start the next row (Fig. 3.36).

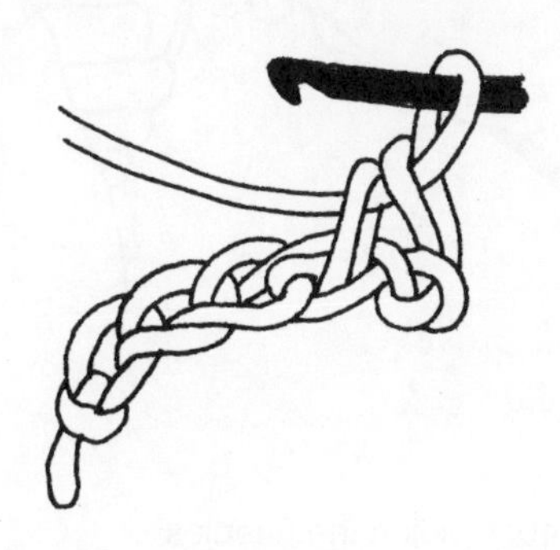

Fig. 3.36 Starting the next row

(12) See if you can make a square of double crochet by completing more rows. Your loops will improve with practice and the crocheting will become even.

(13) **Answer the following questions in your workbook**
  (a) Why do you think it is important to do a turning chain before you start each row?
  (b) How could you make the chains larger or smaller?
  (c) What makes crocheting different from weaving?

Activity 3:9 — Extension

Try crocheting a sample large enough to make a hand puppet. Sew on yarn for hair and paste on felt features with fabric glue (Fig. 3.37).

Fig. 3.37 Crocheted puppets

Knitting

Kniting uses a single yarn like crocheting to make a fabric. Articles and clothing can be knitted with a pair of knitting needles, a home knitting-machine or a manufacturing knitting-machine where knitted fabric can be made and put on a roll just like woven fabric.

Activity 3:9 — Knitting

You will need

- A pair of knitting needles [size 5.5 cm is best to start with]
- 8-ply woollen knitting yarn

Method

(1) The first step is to cast on. Make a slip knot on one of the needles (Fig. 3.38).

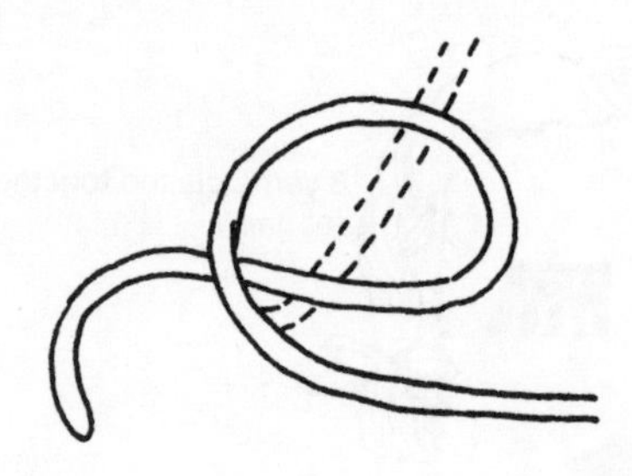

Fig. 3.38 Making a slip knot

(2) Slip the needle into the loop and pull tight (Fig. 3.39). Then, hold the needle in your left hand.

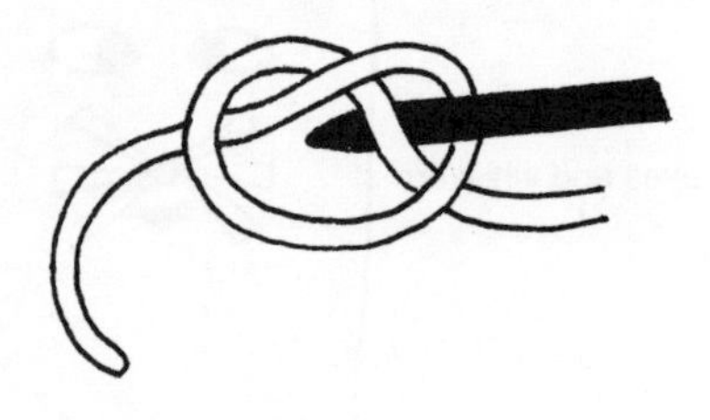

Fig. 3.39 Slipping the needle into the loop

(3) Hold the second needle like a pencil (Fig. 3.40).

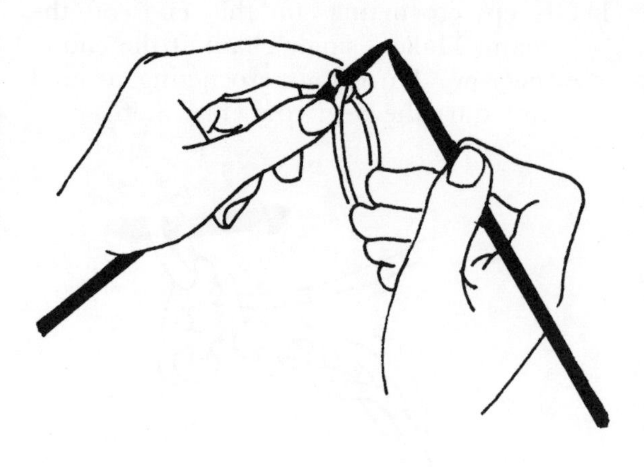

Fig. 3.40 Holding the needles

(4) Push the point of the right-hand needle through the loop (Fig. 3.41).

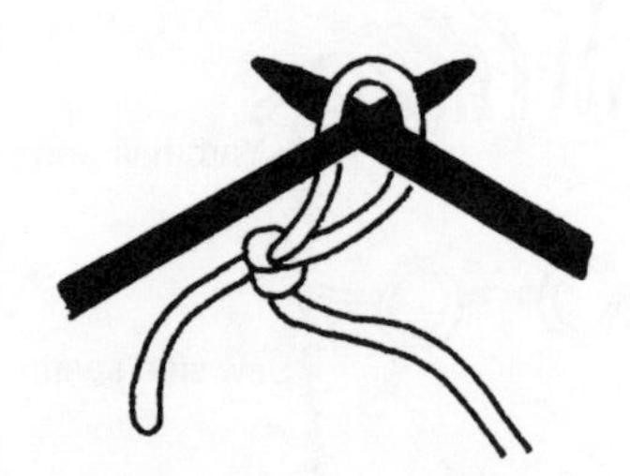

Fig. 3.41 Pushing the needle through the loop

(5) Bring the yarn around the right-hand needle (Fig. 3.42).

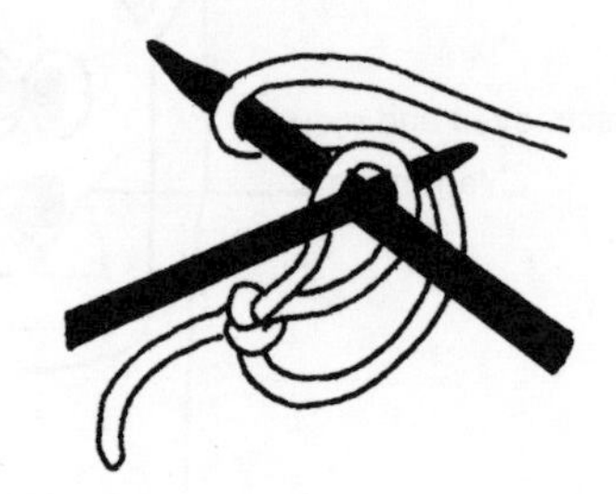

Fig. 3.42 Bringing the yarn around

(6) Pull the new loop through the first loop using the right-hand needle (Fig. 3.43).

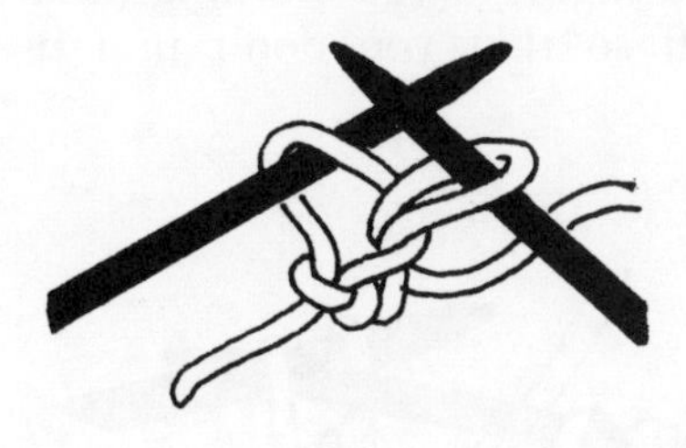

Fig. 3.43 Pulling the new loop through

(7) Slip the new loop onto the left-hand needle.

(8) Push the right-hand needle between t 2 stitches and bring the yarn arou (Fig. 3.44).

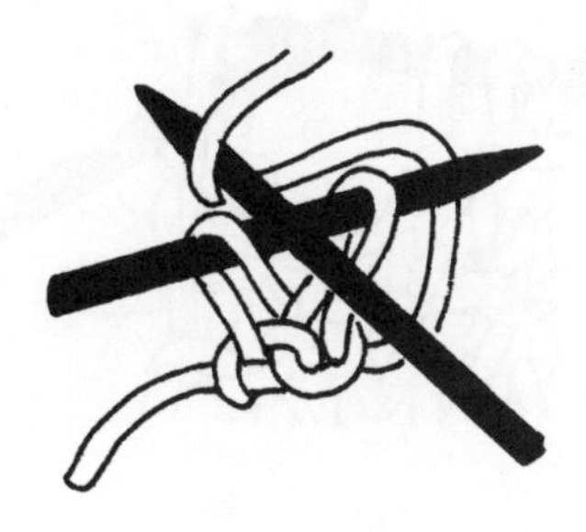

Fig. 3.44 Pushing the yarn between the two loops

(9) Put the new loop onto the left-hand needle (Fig. 3.45).

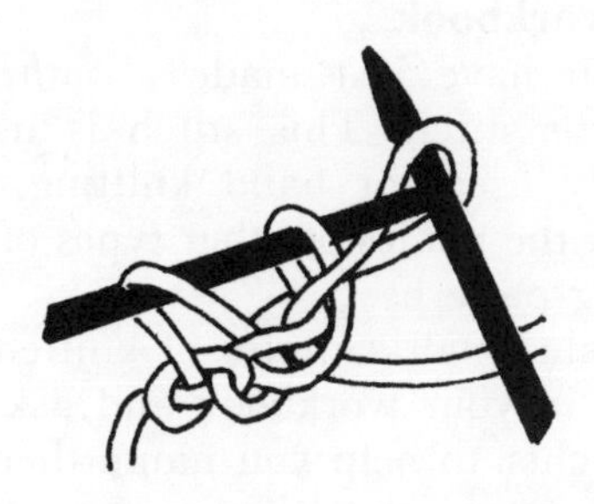

Fig. 3.45 Putting the new loop onto the left-hand needle

(10) Keep casting on until you have 10 stitches (Fig. 3.46).

Fig. 3.46 Ten stitches on the needle

(11) Now you are ready to knit the second row! Put the right-hand needle through the middle of the first stitch (Fig. 3.47).

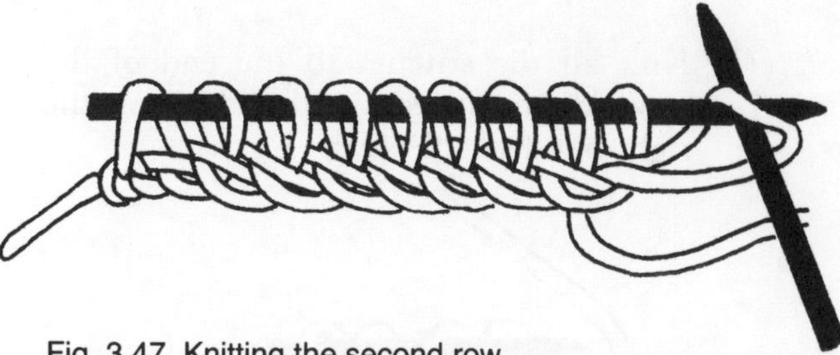

Fig. 3.47 Knitting the second row

(12) Bring the yarn around the top of the needle (Fig. 3.48).

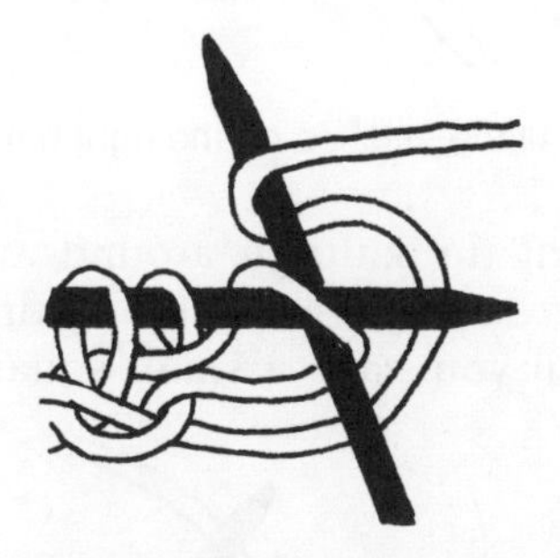

Fig. 3.48 Bringing the yarn around the top of the needle

(13) Pull the loop through using the right-hand needle (Fig. 3.49).

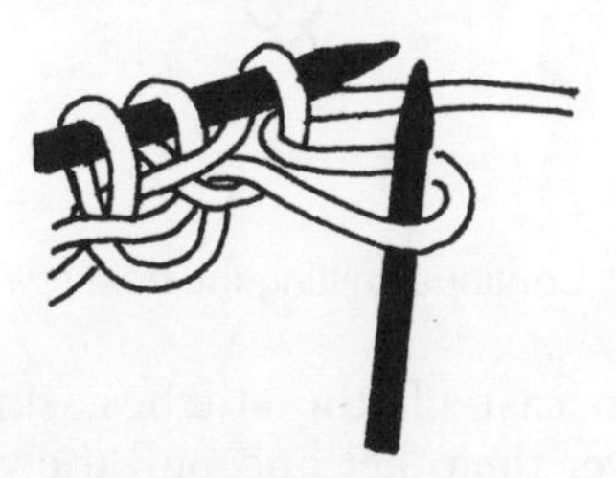

Fig. 3.49 Pulling the loop through

(14) Slip this stitch off onto the right-hand needle (Fig. 3.50).

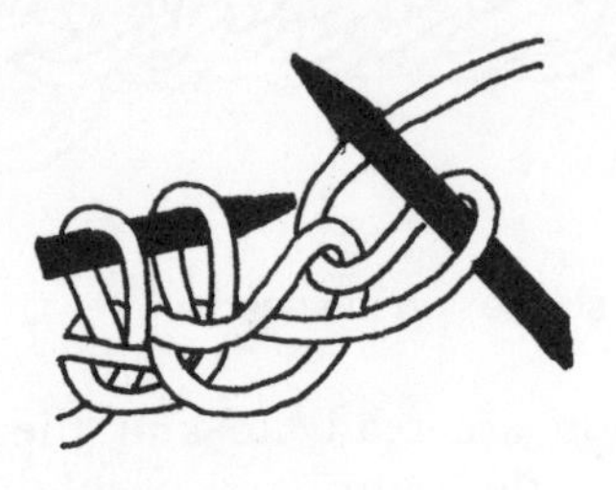

Fig. 3.50 Slipping the stitch off

(15) Knit all the stitches to the end of the row. All the stitches will end up on the right-hand needle (Fig. 3.51).

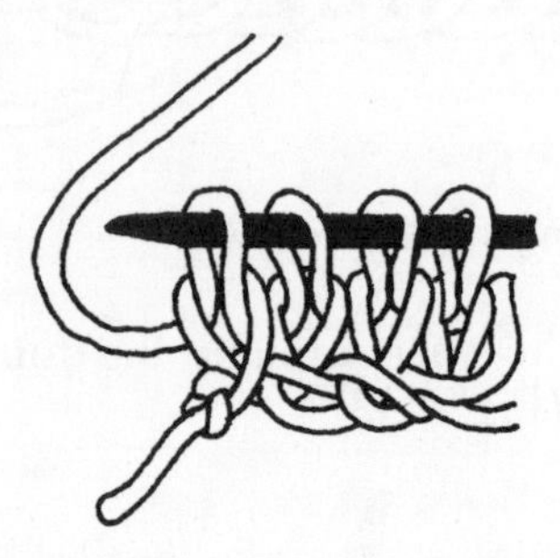

Fig. 3.51 All the stitches on the right hand needle

(16) Turn the knitting around and start the next row (Fig. 3.52). Continue knitting until you have a small square.

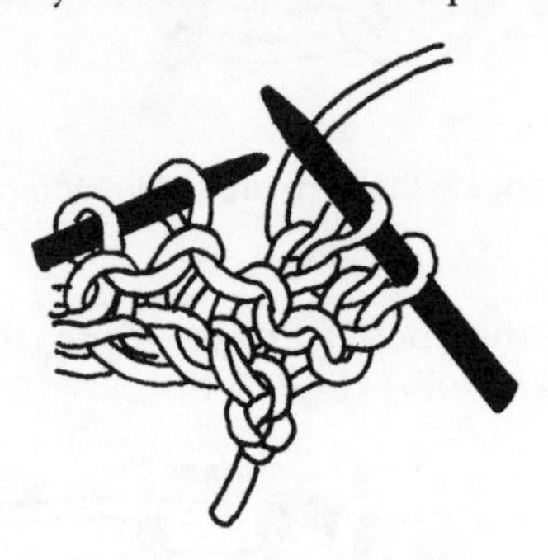

Fig. 3.52 Continue knitting the next row

(17) To cast off the stitches, slip one stitch over the other and pull the yarn through at the end (Fig. 3.53). It is a good idea to use a slightly larger knitting needle to cast off so that you don't pull it too tight.

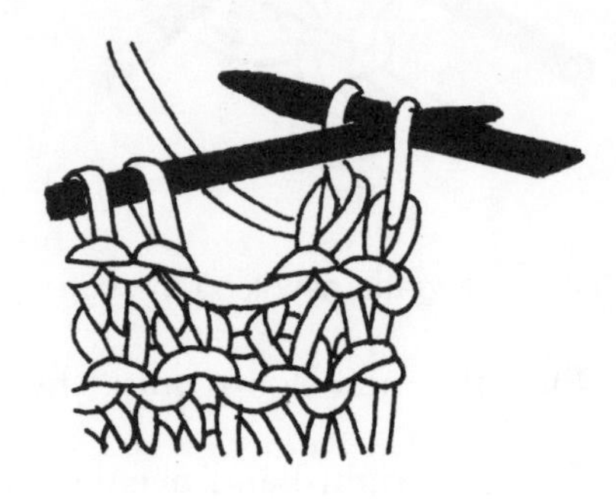

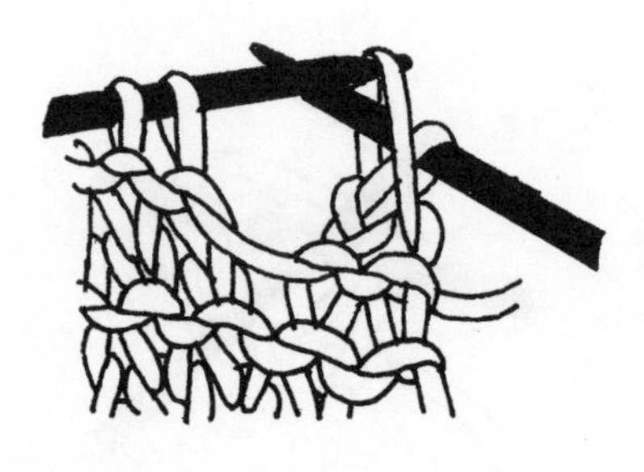

Fig. 3.53 Casting off

(18) **Answer the following questions in your workbook**

(a) You have just made a sample of *garter* stitch. This stitch is usually only used for hand knitting. Find out the names of other types of knitting patterns.
(b) Paste small samples of knitted fabric in your workbook and ask your teacher to help you name them.
(c) What are the differences you can observe between knitted and woven fabrics?
(d) Try making a ladder in a sample of knitted fabric. What happens?
(e) Why can't woven fabrics ladder?
(f) Fill in the table opposite.

Fabric name	Woven/knitted	Use
gaberdine	woven	pants and jackets
rib knit	knitted	
calico		bags
denim		jeans
single knit	knitted	
double knit	knitted	
brushed single knit		sloppy joes
	knitted	socks

(g) Woollen yarn is easy to knit with because it is soft, flexible, and elastic. What other types of yarns are used for hand knitting?

Activity 3:10 — Extension

Try making squares for a patchwork rug. To make a rug, it is important that the same ply wool is used, the same size needles and the same number of stitches are cast on for each square. Why?

If everyone in the class makes a square, then you could sew the rug together by hand and use it in the school clinic or give it to someone needy.

Fig. 3.54 Knitted rug made up of strips — another possibility

Fig. 3.55

Tying

Knotting or macramé is a way of making fabric by tying yarns together in knots. The knots make the fabric open and so it is not usually suitable for clothing. Macramé has many uses including: belts, plant hangers, ropes, dog leads, horse bridles, and key chains.

Activity 3:11 — Key chain

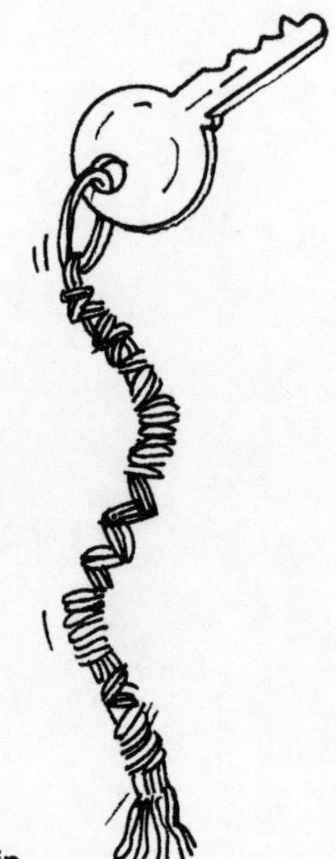

Fig. 3.56 Key chain

You will need

- 140 cm of 2 mm cotton cord
- Scissors
- Key ring

Method

(1) Cut the cord in half, and mount the cords over the key ring with a lark's head knot (Fig. 3.57).

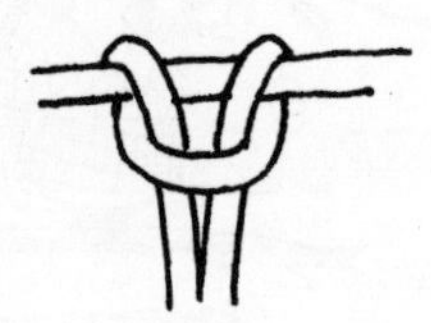

Fig. 3.57 Lark's head knot

(2) Use a half knot to start by tying the 2 outside yarns over the inside filler yarns using a half hitch knot (Fig. 3.58).

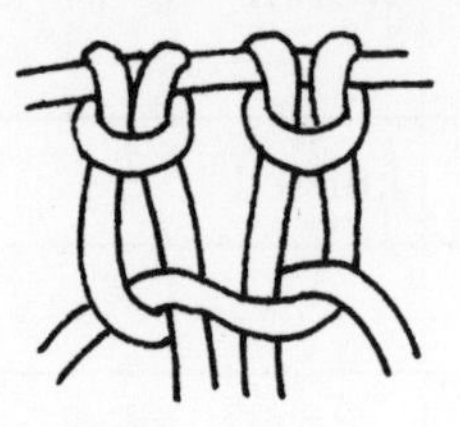

Fig. 3.58 Half hitch knot

(3) Make a square knot by tying the opposite way to the half hitch knot (Fig. 3.59).

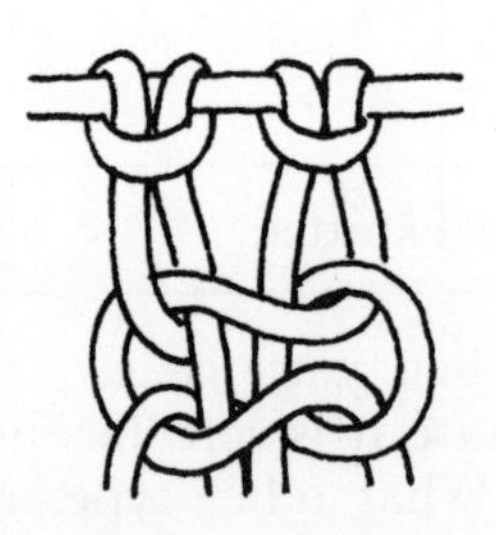

Fig. 3.59 Square knot

(4) Work 8 square knots.
(5) Change the filler cords to the outside and work 20 half hitch knots.
(6) Change the filler cord to the outside and work 8 square knots again.
(7) Work an overhand knot and cut the ends leaving 4 cm of yarn. Tie a small overhand knot at the end of each yarn.

Fig. 3.60 Overhand knot

(8) **Answer the following questions in your workbook**
   (a) What is the difference between the square and half hitch knots in the finished key chain?
   (b) What makes the half hitch knots form a spiral?
   (c) What other types of macramé cords are there?

(d) What is the difference between a filler cord and a knotting cord?
(e) What would happen to the filler cords if they were not used for knotting when you were making the key ring?

Activity 3:12 — Extension

(1) Make up your own designs for macramé by tying different knots and using beads.
(2) Make a belt with square knots every 8 cm, then a bead, then a square knot, then 8 cm and another bead.

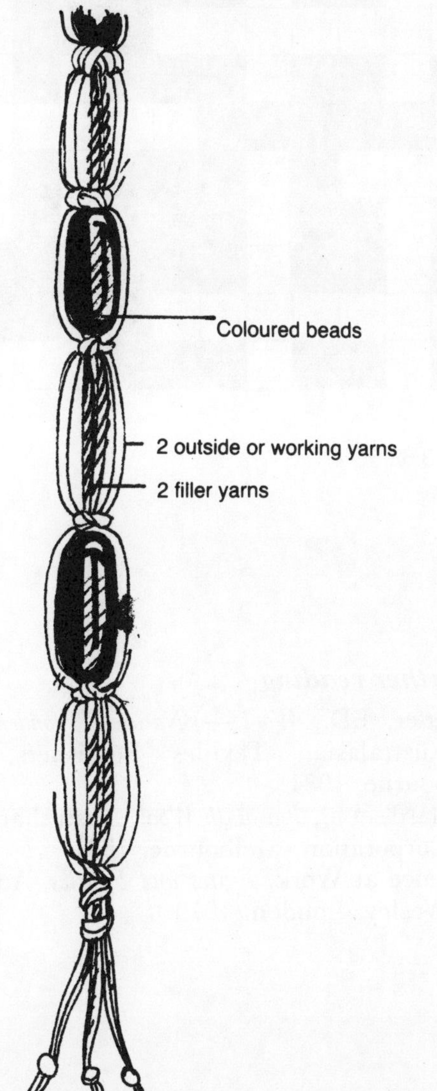

Fig. 3.61 Macramé belt

Words to remember

weaving
weft
warp
loom
macramé
crochet
knitting
fibre
yarn
fabric
felt
vilene
bonded
selvedge
bias
straight grain
garter stitch
lark's head knot
square knot
half hitch knot
overhand knot

Glossary

Asbestos — A fire-resistant mineral fibre.
Flax — A slender, upright plant grown for its fibres and seeds for linseed oil.
Linen — A fabric made from flax.
Cohesion — To stick or stay together.
Flexibility — Easy to move.
Cellulosic — Made from plants.
Synthetic — Produced artificially.
Inorganic — Not containing any carbon compounds.
Spandex — A two-way-stretch elastic fabric.
Lycra — A brand name for a stretch knit fabric used for swimming costumes and exercise wear.
Insulation — A non-conducting fabric which keeps heat and cold out.
Wadding — A fabric insulation.
Acrylic — A synthetic alternative to wool.

Activity 3:12 — Revision

All the answers to the crossword (Fig. 3.62) are in this chapter.

Clues

Down

(1) A non-conducting fabric which keeps heat and cold out
(2) A two-way stretch elastic fabric
(3) A tool for weaving
(4) A process whereby fibres are made into yarn
(5) A type of macramé knot
(6) A synthetic fibre
(7) Yarns are knitted, woven, crocheted, tied, or bonded to make this
(8) 45° angle to the straight grain of a piece of fabric
(9) A way of making fabric by knotting
(10) A type of synthetic fibre used as an alternative to wool
(11) Po-yes-er is a synthetic fibre
(12) Denim is a ______ fabric
(13) The straight ______ runs parallel to the selvedge

Across

(1) Same as 1 down
(2) After a lot of practice, your knitting will become ______
(3) Bonded fabrics are made straight from f--res
(4) You can make this from calico
(5) A d-uble kn-t fabric can be used for making pants and jackets
(6) Disposable ________ are made from bonded fibres
(7) A brand name for a stretch fabric
(8) The answer to 7 across is a ____ way stretch knit fabric
(9) Done on a loom
(10) An egg ____ can be made from felt

Fig. 3.62

Further reading

Leeder, J.D., *Wool — Nature's Wonder Fibre*, Australasian Textiles Publishers, Melbourne, 1984

Pollard, et al, *Fun with Wool*, Australian Wool Corporation, Melbourne, 1981

Science at Work, *Fibres and Fabrics*, Addison-Wesley, London, 1979

4

Design

What is design?

Design is a mental *plan* which has an end in view. It can be a plan for an invention, a piece of art, architecture, or even an aeroplane. Human needs are very important when considering if a design is a good one.

Design is one of the most important factors in our lives, but often one of the least thought about. We are all ruled by the designs of other people. How many times each day do you design for yourself? Make a list of activities in which you are the designer. Fig. 4.1 may give you some ideas.

Fig. 4.1

As you can see, design is many things in many different circumstances. After completing this exercise, you will agree that you too are a designer. You may not carve pieces of sculpture, but you are still a designer because you use the principles of design many times throughout your life. You arrange your room the way you want and you select clothing that makes you look good and feel comfortable. You are a designer!

Let's look at the design of a pillowcase. It is important to make sure that the fabric is easily laundered, is long-lasting, that it fits the pillow without being too large or too small, and that it provides a fold-over piece of fabric to make the pillow stay in its case. Did you ever stop to think that all these problems were related to designing pillowcases?

Fig. 4.2 Pillowcase design

Being able to think clearly about all the problems before you design something is very important in making sure that the end product is *functional*. This means that the article you have designed suits the purpose for which it was intended.

Activity 4:1

Fig. 4.3 A symbolic cake

- Most people agree that the main function of a cake is for eating. The cake in Fig. 4.3 is for celebrating, it is *symbolic*. Try to think of other examples where *function* is exchanged for *symbolism*.
- What are the problems to consider before you begin designing each of the following:
- A school shirt
- A fishing rod
- A school bag

Write the answers in your workbook.

What is good design?

The three rules of good design are:

(1) The design must meet the needs of the product being made. For example, a cake must be able to be eaten.

(2) The cost of the result must be reasonable for the type of product and its value to purchasers. For example, a cake which cost $1000 to make would outweigh its value to most people.

(3) The appearance of the product must be acceptable. It must look pleasing to the eye and be appealing. For example, a cake which is sunken in the centre, like the cake in Fig. 4.4, does not look appealing.

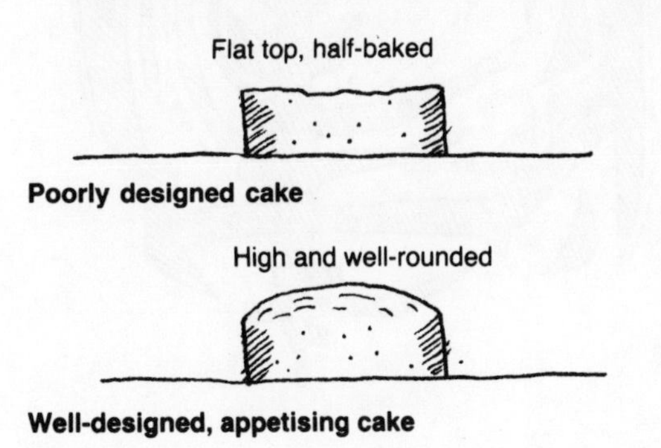

Fig. 4.4

Activity 4:2

Have you ever designed anything which you considered to be poor or unacceptable? If so, what do you think was the problem? Try to work out what went wrong so that you don't make the same wrong design decision again. Make a plan of action in your workbook to ensure that your design works next time.

You can be a good designer or craftsperson by practising your design skills. The more practice you have, the better you will become. In prehistoric times, people met the daily routine needs of cooking, storing, carrying and clothing themselves with very functional design. Later, people began to think about the creativeness of the products they were producing. Many cooking utensils, for example, became *functional* as well as *decorative* or *creative* (Fig. 4.5)

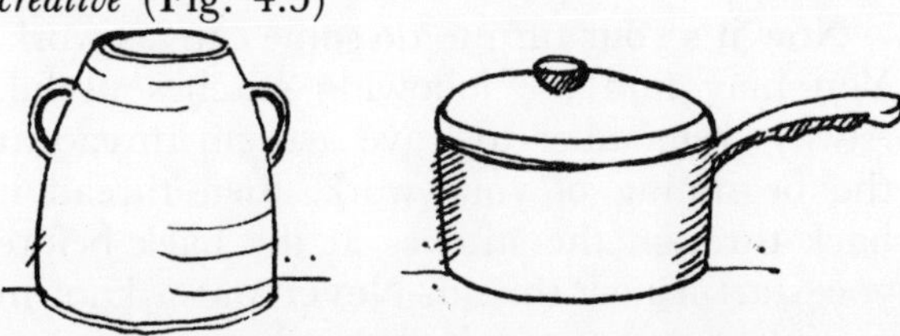

Fig. 4.5 An ancient cooking pot and a modern saucepan

Activity 4:3

Which parts of clothing on the two men in Fig. 4.6 are functional, and which are purely decorative?

Fig. 4.6

Fig. 4.7 American Indian cushion design

Fig. 4.8 Abstract design for a rose

The abstract rose (Fig. 4.8) has red fabric pieces cut out and placed on a cream coloured background. A large tacking stitch makes the curved lines flow smoothly. The cat and kitten (Fig. 4.9) show simple outlines of black on a white background. Black pen is used for the whiskers and kitten outline, while embroidery provides decoration.

Fig. 4.9

Now it's your turn to do some collage.

You will need

- Scissors
- Paper and pencil to plan your design
- Fabric scraps
- Thick card or masonite as a backing board
- Fabric glue
- Ink or embroidery thread for decoration if required

Remember to plan your design carefully, thinking about the problems you will have to overcome in order to produce an aesthetically pleasing piece of work.

Activity 4:5 Canvas work

Canvas work uses stitches to fill in an open-weave fabric to make a design. You can use simple stitches or a variety of stitches to produce different textures. The examples of canvas work shown in Fig. 4.10 may provide you with inspiration for your own design.

Now it's your turn to do some canvas work. You may find the following stitches useful. Always remember to leave a 6 cm thread at the beginning of your work, then thread it back through the stitches at the back before you start a new thread. **Never** put a knot in your work to start as it gives a lumpy, uneven appearance and the work cannot then be framed or made into a useful article.

Fig. 4.10 American Indian needlepoint designs for cushions

You will need

- Pencil and graph paper
- A blunt needle with a large hole, such as a tapestry needle
- Scissors
- Masking tape for the edges of the canvas so that it doesn't unravel while you are working on it
- Canvas which is firm, and has an even weave [5 threads per cm] and has single threads
- 8-ply woollen yarn

Planning the design

(1) First of all, think about the colours and textures that you want to portray.

(2) Both the canvas and stitches suggest geometric shapes. So, work out a scale on your graph paper which will represent the canvas. Use coloured pencils to indicate the different colours used in your design.

(3) The graph shown in Fig. 4.11 shows a design for some canvas work. Squares, dots and crosses represent the different colours used. Where the arrows meet in the centre is the starting point for the first stitch.

(4) After you have mapped out your design on graph paper, practise the stitches you have chosen to complete the work.

Look through the stitch designs in Fig. 4.13 to give you some ideas.

Choose colours carefully so that they look good together and make the design aesthetically pleasing.

Squares, dots and crosses represent the different colours used.

Where the arrows meet indicates the centre of the design on the fabric.

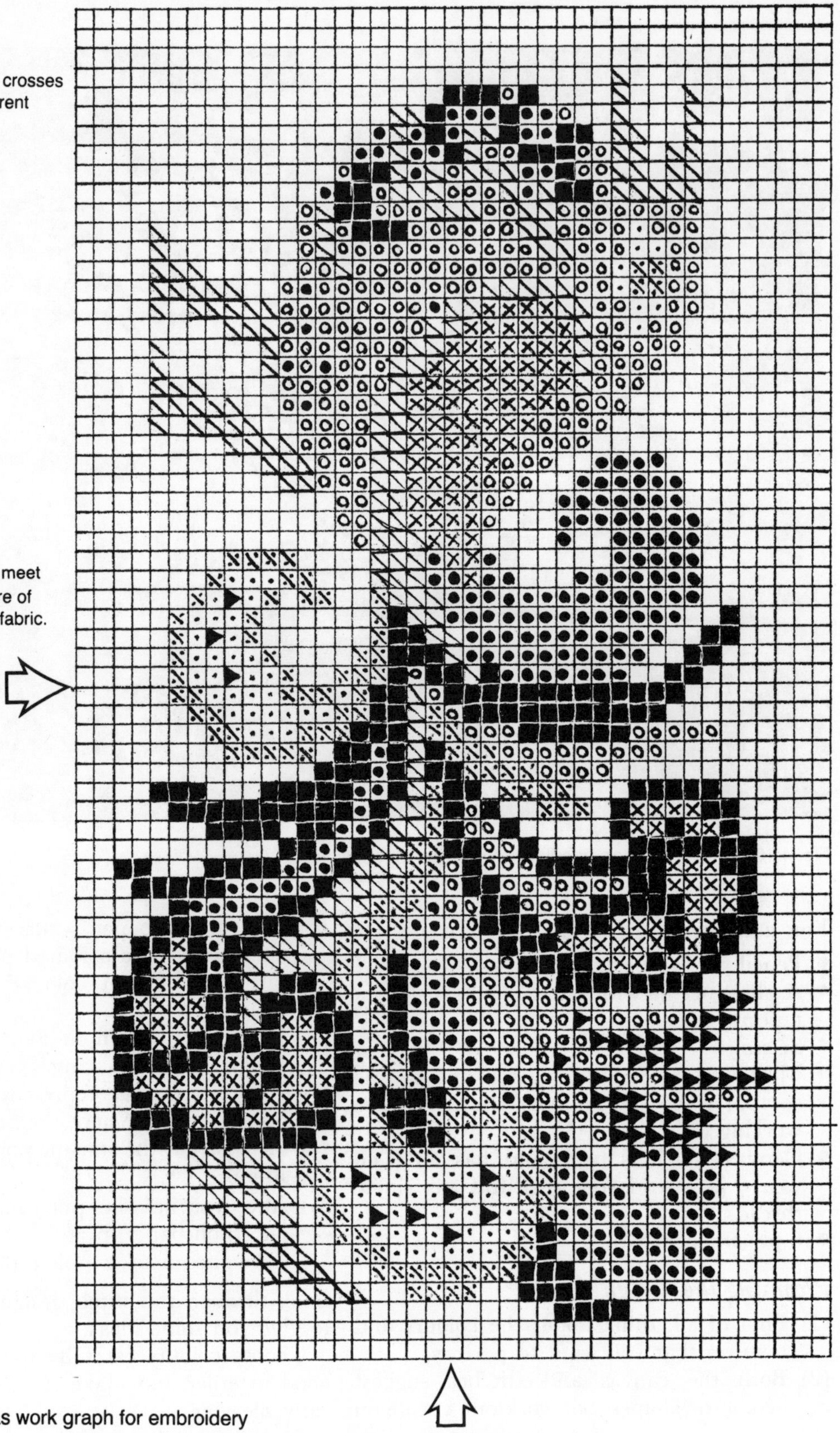

Fig. 4.11 Canvas work graph for embroidery

Fig. 4.12 Completed canvas work

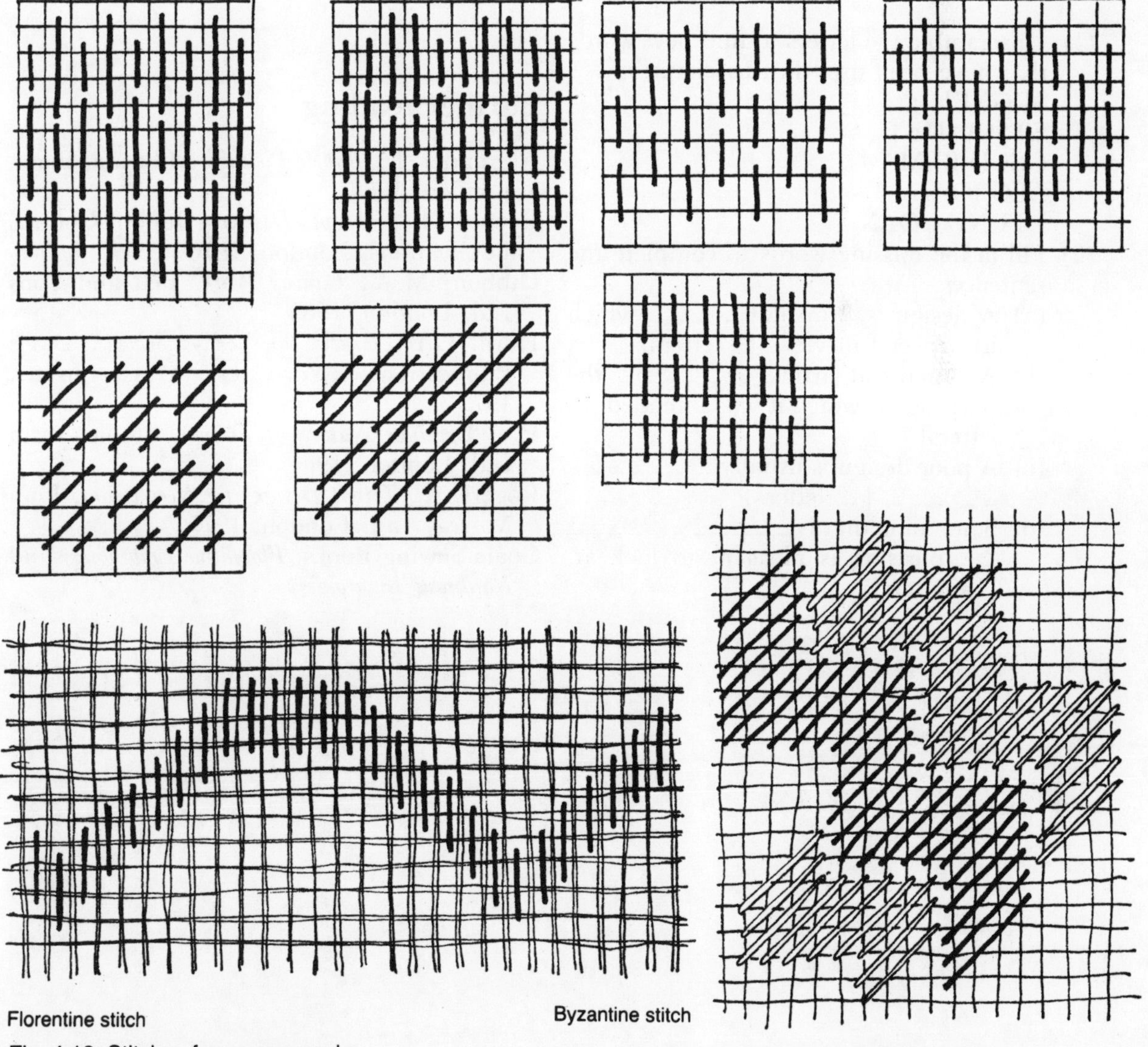

Fig. 4.13 Stitches for canvas work

Words to remember

design
functional
aesthetic
aesthetically
symbolic
decorative
creative
collage
embroidery
geometric

Activity 4:6 — Revision

(1) Unscramble the letters to find new words that have been used in this chapter.
SDGNEI
ETSCIAHET
OSCIYBLM
LECGOAL
LTUNIFCOAN

(2) Fill in the missing words to complete the sentences.
(a) A design is a mental _ _ _ _ which has an end in view. [4 letters]
(b) A functional article _ _ _ _ _ the purpose for which it was intended. [5 letters]
(c) A poor design is usually _ _ _ _ _ _ _ _ _ _ _ _. [12 letters]
(d) Something that is _ _ _ _ _ _ _ _ _ _ _ _ _ pleasing is pleasant to look at. [13 letters]
(e) _ _ _ _ _ _ _ is another name for pictures made of fabric. [7 letters]

Glossary

Decorative — Attractive as well as, or rather than, functional.
Design — A mental plan which has an end in view.
Functional — The article suits the purpose for which it was intended.
Geometric — A linear design.
Symbolic — Representing something.

Further reading

Alexander, E., *Fabric Pictures*, Mills and Boon, London, 1967
Baynes, K., *About Design*, Design Council Publications, London, 1976
Gibbon, M.A., *Canvas Work*, Bell and Sons Ltd, London, 1965
Horn, G.F., *Crafts for Todays Schools*, Davis Publications, Worcester, Massachusetts, 1972
Pye, D., *The Nature of Design*, Studio Vista Ltd, London, 1964
Rogers, A., *Tribal Designs for Needlepoint*, John Murray Ltd, London, 1977
Coats Sewing Books: *Florentine Embroidery* and *Norweave Embroidery*

5

Style in a package

When a decision is made to sew an article, two choices exist: we can make our own pattern which takes time and skill we do not always have or we can buy a pattern. Most people, because of time and lack of skill, choose to buy a pattern from a shop. These patterns are known as *commercial patterns*. Each season, the companies that produce commercial patterns put out a new *catalogue* of styles. The pattern books have a range of items to make including clothing, toys, household articles and fancy dress clothes. In order to use these patterns well, some basic information needs to be learnt.

Fig. 5.1 The commercial pattern section of a department store

The pattern envelope

When a pattern is purchased, it has three elements:

- The envelope
- The sewing direction sheet
- Tissue pattern pieces

All three contain essential information needed to make sewing accurate and easy.

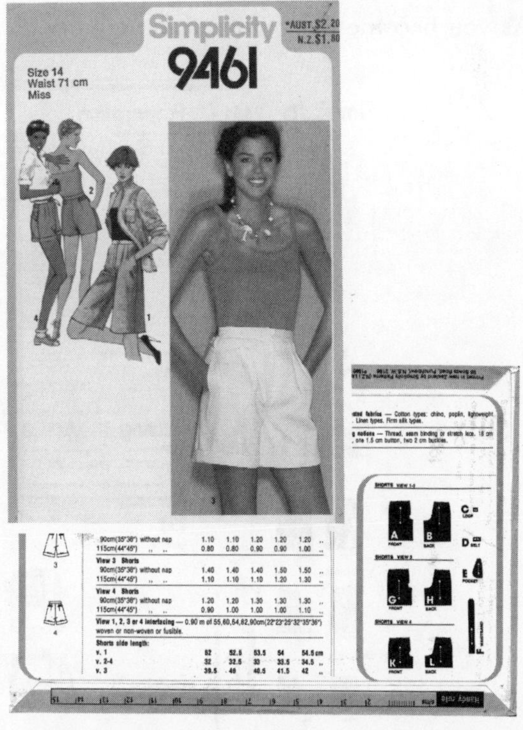

Fig. 5.2 Pattern envelope — front and back

The envelope

Front — On the front of the envelope is a picture or illustration of the style. The size, brand name and style variations are also on the front.

Back — The back of a pattern envelope has information to help purchase the correct fabric and equipment.

Garment description — Details of the style chosen. These details are not always visible on the diagram or illustration.

Fabric — Some styles may be made from striped or plaid fabric; if so, extra advice on fabric is required.

Standard body measurements — The size of a pattern is determined by the body measurements on the back of the envelope. Because everybody is different, it is necessary to check your measurements with the envelope measurements. This will help ensure you do not sew an article that is too big or too small.

The number of pattern pieces — This is shown directly under the style number. Patterns with fewer pieces are easier and quicker to sew.

As you become more skilled and confident, start to use patterns with more pieces.

The meterage chart — This chart shows the amount of fabric needed for different views. Fabric comes in different widths, ie. 95 cm, 115 cm, and 145 cm. Check the width so you buy enough. Some articles will need interfacing, elastic and trimmings.

Finished garment measurements — These are the finished back length and the width at the lower edge of the skirt, shirt or trousers.

Sewing notions — Sewing notions are the items you need to complete an article. They may include: threads, elastic, zippers, buttons, shoulder padding.

Suggested fabric — A list is given to select from. These are given as a guide. Select the fabric carefully as it can effect the success of the article.

Back views — Line drawings to illustrate the back view that cannot easily be seen.

Nap — The pattern envelope states '*with nap*' or '*without nap*'. Fabrics that have a nap include corduroy and velvet and one way patterns. You may need to buy extra fabric to make articles selected in these fabrics.

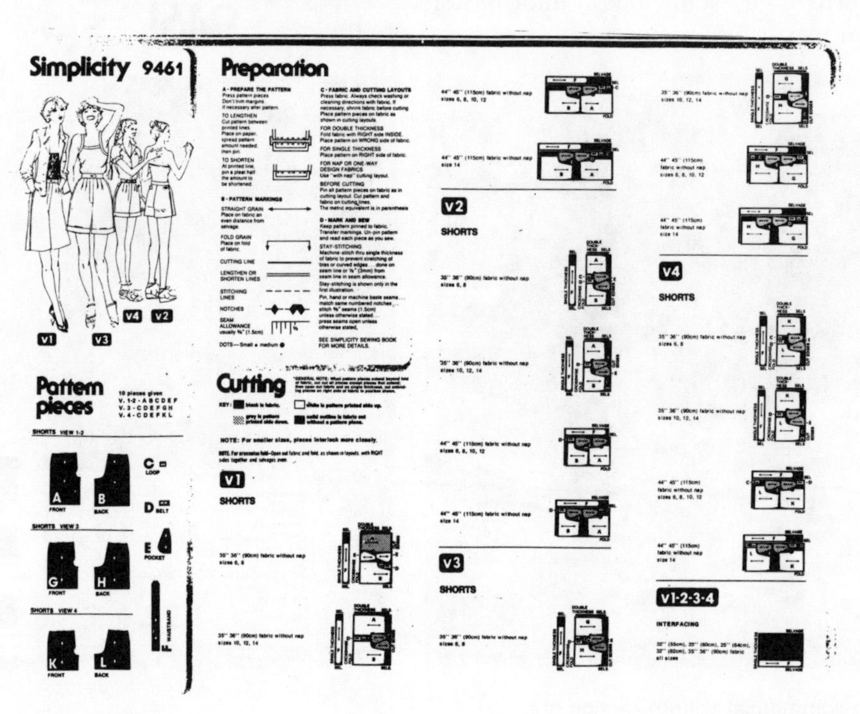

Fig. 5.3 Cutting direction sheet

Cutting and sewing direction sheet

Line drawings of the styles have the pattern pieces needed to make them shown underneath (Fig. 5.3).

Cutting layouts — Find the article you are making on the sewing direction sheet. Having collected all the pattern pieces to make the article, lay them on the fabric as shown on the sewing direction sheet.

Sewing directions — These step-by-step directions will take you through the stages of construction.

Tissue pattern pieces

Identification of markings — These are printed on each pattern and include:

- Style number
- Size
- Identification
- View number

Lengthen or shorten here — Instructions to "lengthen or shorten here" are given so patterns can be adjusted. Remember if you alter one pattern piece, you will have to alter the others as well.

Centre front and centre back — Clearly marked on patterns.

Grainline Markings — These are straight lines with arrowheads at each end. In most cases the line is placed on the lengthwise grain of the fabric.

Construction markings

The seamline — Shown as a broken line, 1.5 cm from the cutting line.

Notches — Diamond-shaped symbols along the cutting line. These indicate where the pattern pieces should join.

Arrow — These are often on the seamline. They show the direction you should sew.

Darts — Two broken lines with a solid line down the centre. These lines help you fold the dart correctly.

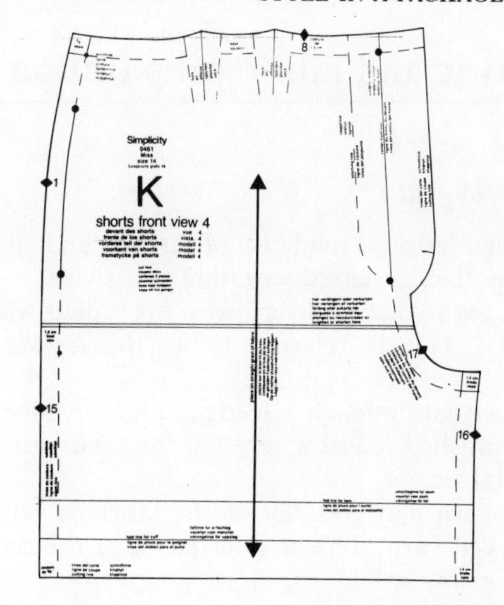

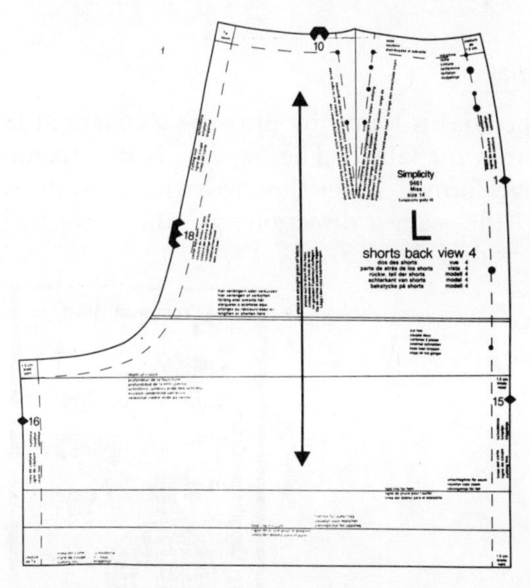

Fig. 5.4 Pattern pieces with instructions for construction

Buttonholes — Indicated by a solid line and a short line at right angles.

Solid lines — These show fold lines, some hemlines and placement for pockets and trimmings.

Clip — The cutting of seams to allow the fabric to sit flat.

Gathering or easing — Shown as a broken line.

Pleats — Shown as a solid then a broken line. Arrows show the direction of the pleating.

Fabric and fabric preparation

Fabric grain

Woven fabric is made up of threads known as yarns that go lengthwise and crosswise.
The yarns that go lengthwise are called warp yarns. This is referred to as the *lengthwise grain.*
Woven fabric has a selvedge. The selvedge is the finished lengthwise edge on each side of the fabric.
The yarn that goes across the fabric is called the weft yarn. This is referred to as the *crosswise grain.*

Bias

The Bias is found by drawing a diagonal line across the fabric. The *true bias* is the diagonal edge formed when the crosswise threads run in the same direction as the lengthwise threads (Fig. 5.5).

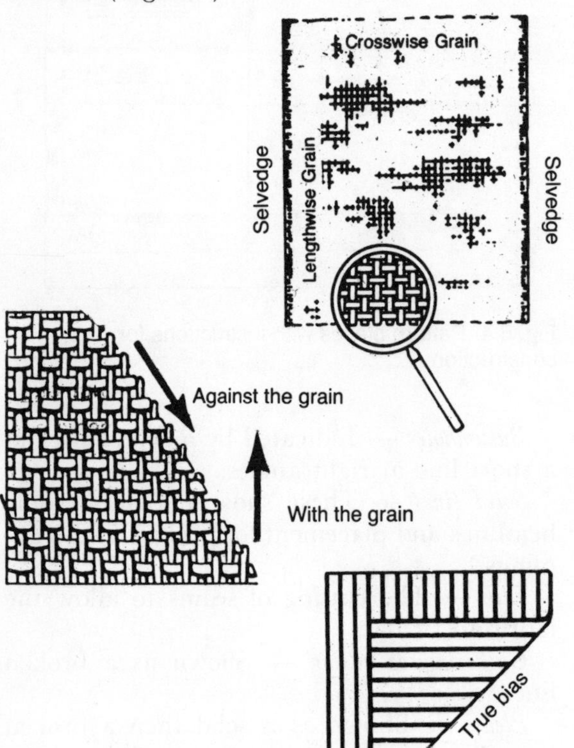

Fig. 5.5 Grainlines

Preparing fabric for cutting

Most off-grain fabrics can easily be straightened by pulling the fabric in the opposite direction of the off-grain slant.
Fabrics that can be washed should be washed to allow for relaxation shrinkage. At this stage, straighten and when dry, press the fabric.
Pressing torn edges
When fabric has been torn, the raw edges should be pressed. Check that the grain is straight.

How to pin

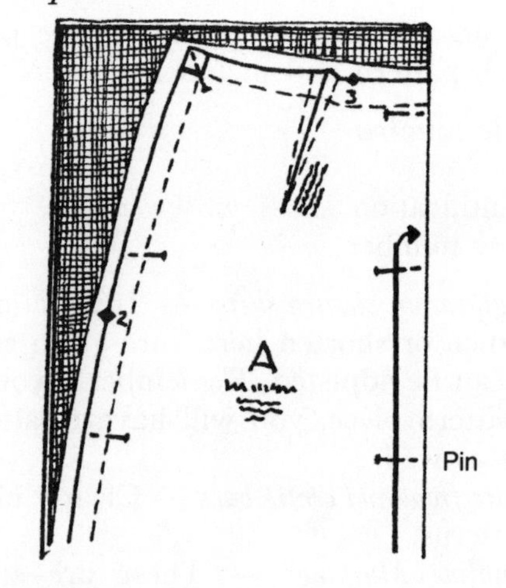

Fig. 5.6 How to pin

Pick up only a few threads of your fabric with each pin so the fabric will lie flat (Fig. 5.6). Do not allow the pins to extend beyond the cutting edge. All pattern pieces must be placed on the grain. Check this as patterns are pinned onto the fabric.

How to cut

Hold the fabric flat on the table. Place your hand on the fabric to keep it flat. Use your other hand to cut the fabric (Fig. 5.7). Cut the notches on the pattern *outwards.* After cutting, leave the patterns pinned to the fabric for making darts and pleats etc.

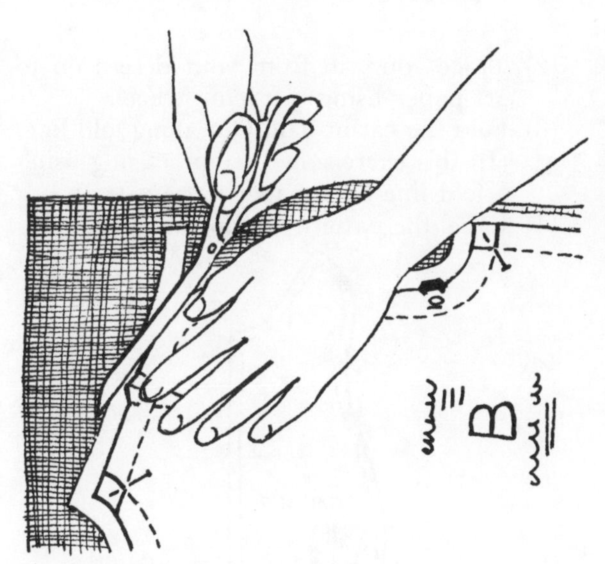

Fig. 5.7 How to cut

Cutting one-way fabrics

Fig. 5.8 One-way fabric

All the pattern pieces must go in the same direction on one-way fabrics as shown in Fig. 5.8.

What to mark

It is necessary to transfer symbols for construction from the pattern to the fabric. Markings are your guide for sewing details accurately.

Transfer all the construction markings that will help you to sew your garment. It is a good idea for beginners to mark curved seams as these can be difficult to sew.

Other markings may include:

- Darts
- Buttonholes
- Pockets
- Trims
- Interfacing

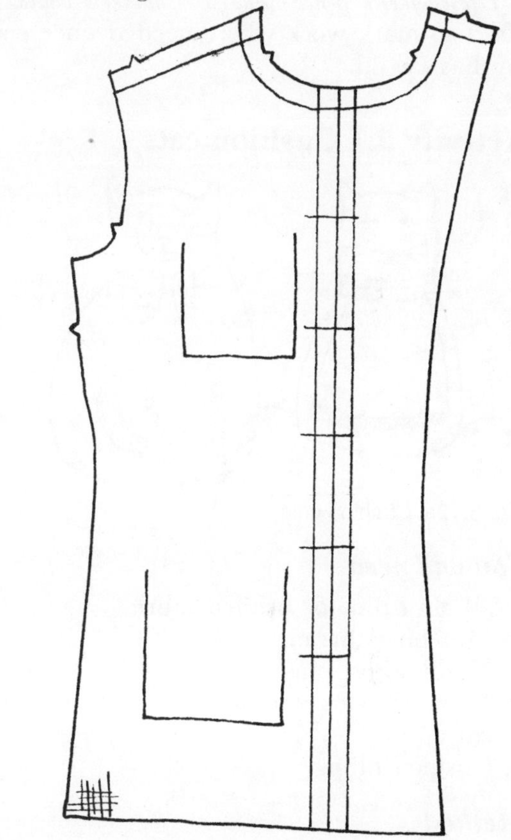

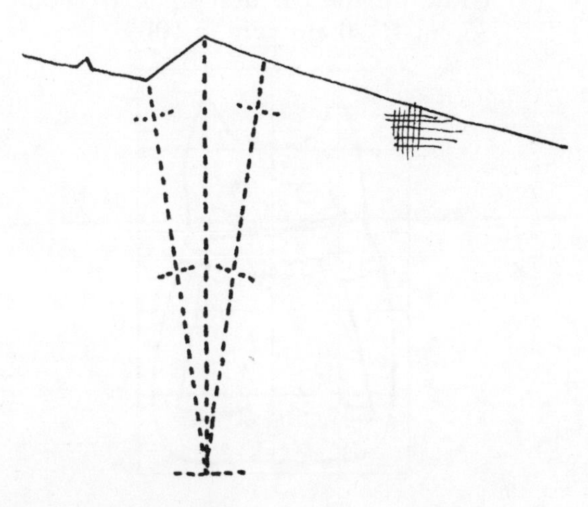

Fig. 5.9 What to mark

Marking fabric

Dressmaker's carbon and tracing wheel — With the carbon side on the fabric and the pattern on top, you can trace around the marks you want to transfer.

Dressmaker's pencils and dressmaker's chalk — Used to mark work where needed once sewing has begun.

Activity 5:1 Cushion cats

Fig. 5.10a Cushion cats

You will need

- 50 cm calico or printed fabric
- Matching thread
- Needles and pins
- Extra ribbons and fabric to decorate the cat
- Cushion filling

Method

(1) Draw up the cat design in a rectangle 35 cm × 20 cm (Fig. 5.10b).

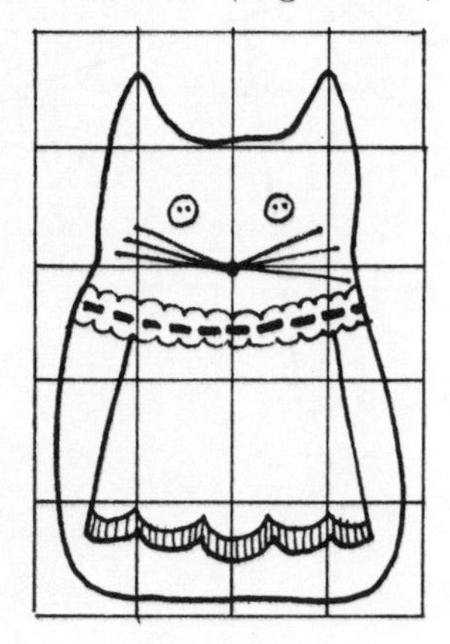

Fig. 5.10b Grid for cat cushion

(2) Trace your cat from your design on to art paper using a tracing wheel.

(3) Fold the cat in half. Cut along fold line. (In this exercise we are practising using a fold line on a paper pattern.)

(4) Label the pattern as shown in Fig. 5.11.

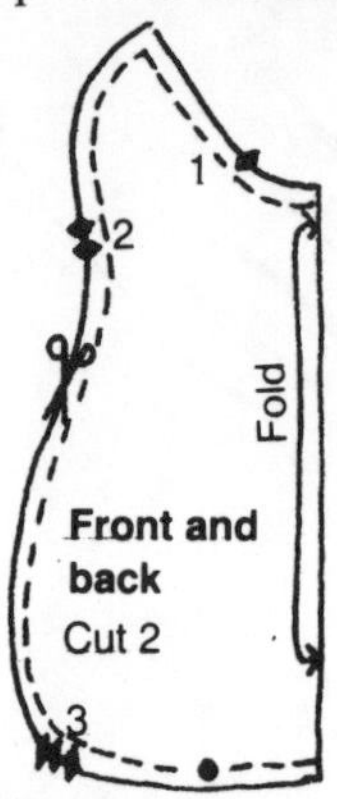

Fig. 5.11 Cat pattern labelling

(5) Place on fabric as shown in *fabric layout* (Fig. 5.12).

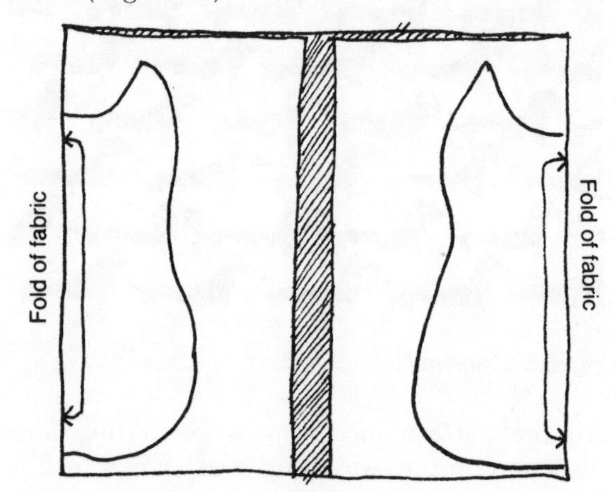

Fig. 5.12 Layout of cat pattern

(6) Before sewing the front and back of the cushion together, decorate the front of the cushion. Small pieces of lace, ribbon, buttons, wool, felt and fabric can be used. Glue or sew decoration on to the front pattern.

(7) Put the two right sides of the cushion together. Pin all the way around (Fig. 5.13). Leave an opening between the dots at the bottom of the cushion.

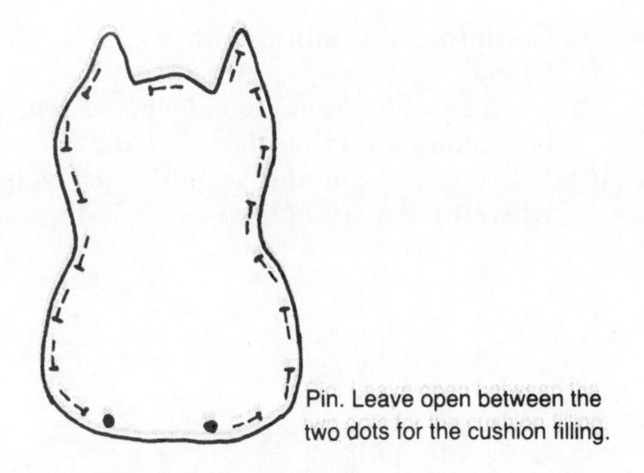

Fig. 5.13 Pinning pattern

(8) Sew 2 rows of machine stitching around the cushion for strength.
(9) Trim and clip the edges so the cushion will turn inside out easily (Fig. 5.14).

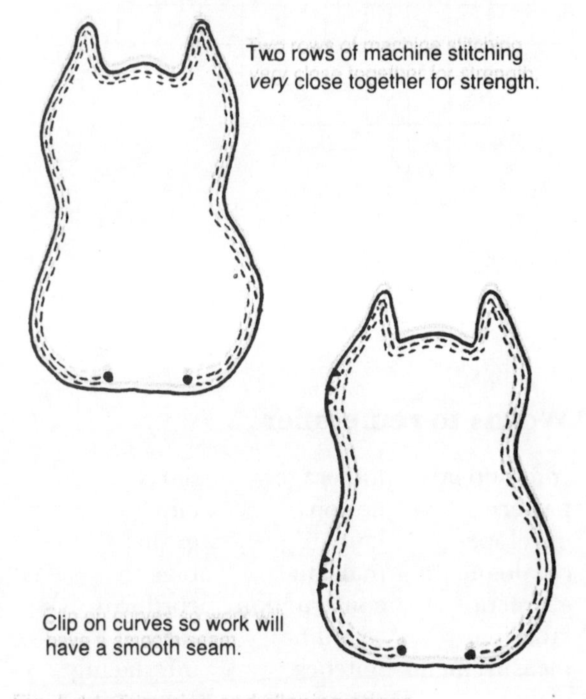

Fig. 5.14 Trimming and clipping edges

(10) Press.
(11) Fill cushion until it is firmly packed with cushion filling.
(12) Topstitch the opening of the cushion using the same colour threads.

To make a cat family, use a variety of bits and pieces that are left over.

Activity 5:2 — Extension

(1) Obtain a large white envelope. This will become the pattern envelope for the cushion cat. Draw on the front and back of the envelope all the information that would be found on a commercial pattern if you purchased this in a store.
(2) Construct a sewing direction sheet (look back in the chapter for help with this).
(3) Draw up a new pattern for the cushion.
(4) Hand your teacher the completed cushion cat and the pattern envelope for marking.

Activity 5:3 — Extension

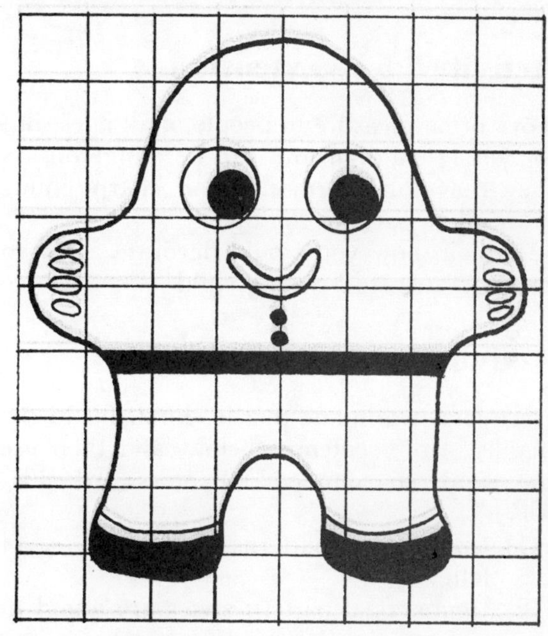

Fig. 5.15 Clown

Using the clown illustrated in Fig. 5.15:
(1) Draw the pattern pieces used to make the clown.
(2) Label each pattern piece with all the things a commercial pattern would have on it.
(3) Design an instruction sheet. On the instruction sheet give each step needed to construct the clown.
(4) Construct the clown. Remember you can add further decoration if you wish.

Activity 5:4 — Extension

(1) Draw a chart like the following in your workbook, and work out how much one of your toys cost to make.

Material used	Cost

(2) How much would a similar toy, bought in a shop, cost?
(3) Which toy is cheaper?
(4) What are the advantages of making toys?

Activity 5:5 — Extension

Toys bring pleasure to people of all ages, but for young children toys can be dangerous as they may hurt themselves on sharp points or swallow parts of the toy.

Explain how you would decorate a toy to prevent harm to a young child.

Activity 5:6 — Extension

Here is a two-in-one puzzle. First, fill in the blanks in the sentences below, and then use the words to complete the crossword (Fig. 5.17).

(1) Commercial patterns save _ _ _ _. [4 letters]
(2) Commercial pattern styles are found in a _ _ _ _ _ _ _ _ _. [9 letters]
(3) Pattern pieces are made of _ _ _ _ _ _ paper. [6 letters]
(4) Construction information is found on a _ _ _ _ _ _ direction sheet. [6 letters]
(5) _ _ _ _ _ _ may be striped or plaid. [6 letters]
(6) _ _ _ _ measurements tell you the size to buy. [4 letters]
(7) Sewing _ _ _ _ _ _ _ include threads and zippers. [7 letters]
(8) Corduroy is a fabric with a _ _ _. [3 letters]
(9) _ _ _ _ _ _ _ are diamond-shaped symbols along a cutting line. [7 letters]
(10) _ _ _ _ _ _ on the seamline tell you where to sew. [6 letters]

Fig. 5.16

Words to remember

commercial, pattern, envelope, catalogue, garment, fabric, measurement, pieces, meterage, notions, layouts, markings, construction, seamline, notches, arrow, darts, clip, grain, bias, corduroy, carbon, interfacing

Further reading

Simplicity Sewing Book, London, 1975

6

Textiles and the consumer

We are all consumers because every one of us uses *goods* and *services* provided by others. For example, we all eat food supplied to supermarkets by manufacturers, and we all use the services of other people such as electricians or doctors. Most people work hard to earn money, and so we should make sure that every dollar we spend is worth the value of the goods or services we are purchasing.

Fig. 6.1 Goods and services

Activity 6:1

Using a table similar to the following, make a list of all the goods and services you would use in one day. If this exercise takes you more than 10 minutes, then you would probably agree that people living in Australia certainly rely on goods and services provided by others.

Goods	Services

Fig. 6.2 A person making a decision about clothing

Shopping

Life is not easy, even for people who consider themselves expert in shopping. There are many more products to choose from than ever before. Advertising, credit cards, packaging, guarantees written in fine print, fashion styles and inadequate information about what exactly you are purchasing can make shopping a confusing and difficult task. It's no wonder that rash decisions are easy to make which we may come to regret later.

If you consider your choice wisely and shop around for the best price, you will be well on the way to being a responsible consumer.

Many items are much cheaper to buy than they are to make. For example, by the time you have purchased fabric, buttons, thread and a pattern to make a shirt, it might cost $25.00. You could buy a shirt for this amount at most shops. But your decision to make or buy clothes goes much deeper than that. The advantages of making clothes include the satisfaction of creating your own outfits, getting a good fit, and having a large selection of fabrics to choose from.

Fashion clothes for teenagers are often very expensive as manufacturers rely on the teenager's need to conform to the latest fashion. This is where you can save a lot of money by making your own very fashionable clothes for much less than in the shops.

Can you tell which shirt in Fig. 6.3 is home-made? The one on the right was bought in a jeans shop for $50.00. The one on the left was made for half the price.

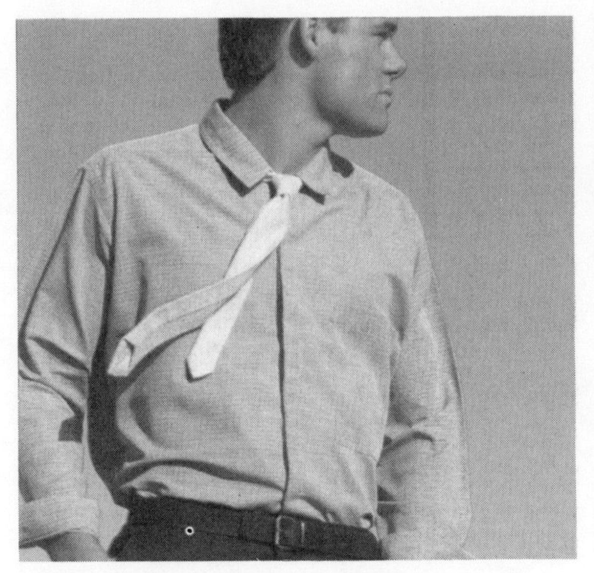

Fig. 6.3 Fashion shirts

Activity 6:2 — Making a pencil case

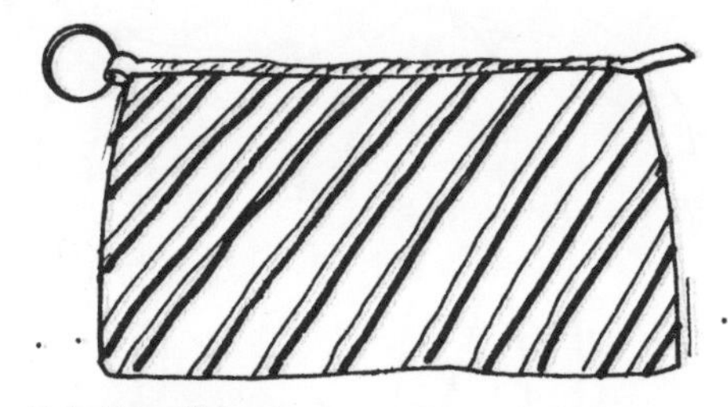

Fig. 6.4 Pencil case

You will need

- 20 cm zipper
- 2 pieces of strong fabric like corduroy, denim or cotton drill, 22 × 14 cm
- Curtain ring
- Sewing thread to match the zipper

Method

(1) Press fabric and zipper flat with the iron.
(2) Sew zipper into place following the guide in Fig. 6.5.
(3) Turn over the 2 pieces of fabric, making sure they are inside out.
(4) Pin, then sew around the 3 sides, 1 cm from the edge.
(5) Zigzag the seams together to prevent fraying.

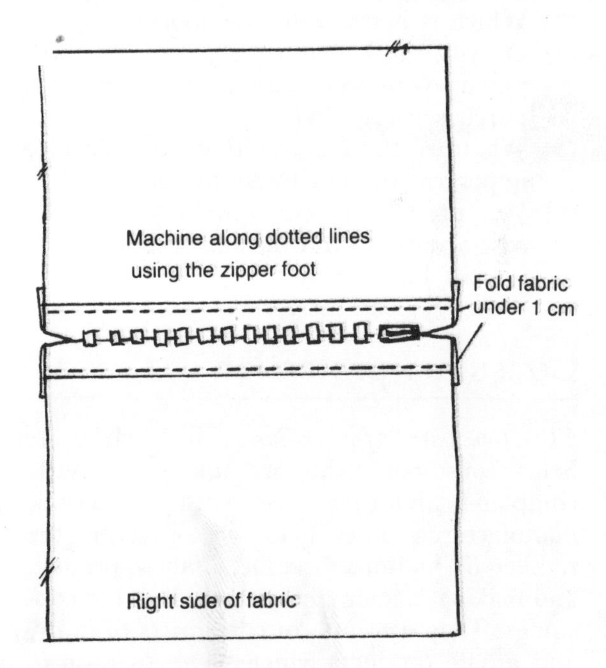

Fig. 6.5 Sewing zipper to the two pieces of fabric

(6) Undo the zip, then turn the case through, pushing out the corners with the blunt end of a pencil.
(7) Place the curtain ring on the end of the zipper catch. When you have finished your pencil case, answer the questions in the following activity.

Activity 6:3

It is important that we think about the value of our time and effort in hand making textile articles and compare them to the purchased item.

Answer the following questions in your workbook:

(1) List and then add up the price of each of the materials required to make your pencil case.

- Zipper ______
- Thread ______
- Fabric ______
- Curtain ring ______

Total: ______

(2) What is the price of a similar manufactured pencil case?
(3) Which is better value for money?
(4) Do you think that your pencil case will put up with wear and tear as well as a purchased one? Why?
(5) What are the features that you consider important in pencil case design?
(6) Was the time taken to make your pencil case a waste or did the end result make it a satisfying exercise?

Fig. 6.6 'Is that the chair you've been complaining about?'

Consumer protection

The *Consumer Affairs Bureau* in each State helps consumers who are unable to settle complaints about purchases with a retailer or manufacturer. They help by contacting the retailer or manufacturer of a faulty product and making a complaint on behalf of the consumer. They also inform consumers of faulty and unsafe products which have come on to the market.

The Consumer Affairs Bureau does not have many complaints about textile items. However when problems do occur, they are usually caused by the limitations of certain fabrics. For example, a new fabric for a chair cover may not stand up to the wear and tear expected of it. After a couple of years it may look shabby and unattractive. Often the design of an article does not take into account the performance of the textile chosen.

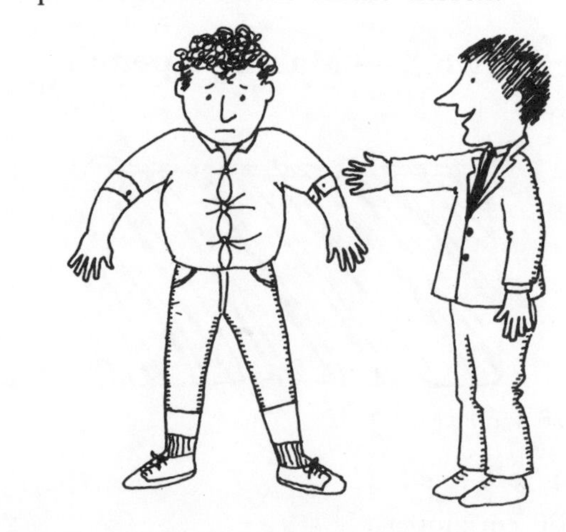

Fig. 6.7 'That fits you perfectly, sir!'

It is important that you read labels carefully before you purchase textile products. What use would an everyday pair of jeans be if they had to be dry-cleaned instead of washed? Be aware of the advice given to you by salespeople. You may end up with a pair of jeans that were sold to you as washable, but when taking a closer look at the label, they can only be dry-cleaned.

Fashionable clothes are often overpriced because retailers know that many people will pay 'anything' to have the latest fashion clothes.

Fig. 6.8 'It's the latest fashion, you know.'

Activity 6:4

Try this experiment to see if some fabrics change their size, or *shrink* when washed.

You will need

- 2 pieces of each fabric to be tested, cut into squares 5 cm × 5 cm (try wool, cotton, polyester and acrylic woven fabrics)
- 1 litre of boiling water in a beaker or saucepan
- Metal spoon or glass stirring rod
- 1 tablespoon of washing detergent

Method

(1) Cut the squares exactly the same size, so that you can compare the sizes before and after washing. Paste the control samples in your workbook, leaving enough room to place the washed sample next to each one. Label the samples with their fibre names e.g. cotton gaberdine.
(2) Dissolve detergent in the boiling water, add the fabric samples and stir occasionally for 10 minutes.
(3) Remove the samples and rinse out all the detergent under a tap.
(4) Dry the samples in the sun or near a heater.
(5) Paste the dry samples in your workbook next to the pre-washed control samples.
(6) Write the new measurement beside each washed sample.
(7) **Answer the following questions under the samples in your workbook.**
 (a) Which fabric shrunk the most?
 (b) Which fabric shrunk the least?
 (c) Which fabrics would you label: '**Dry-clean only**'?
 (d) Which would be the best fabric to make a school shirt from?
 (e) Write down any other interesting observations you made during the experiment. For example, did any fabrics loose their dye in the washing water?
 (f) What is the best temperature for hand washing woollen fabrics? Why?

Informative labelling

There are many textile products that need careful consideration before a wise buying decision can be made. All textiles used in clothing should have a swing tag and a fabric label attached to them (Fig. 6.9). This informs you of the size, manufacturer's name, type of fibres and percentages of each fibre used, and washing instructions. If these things are not on the label, then the manufacturer is not meeting the requirements of the *Australian Standards Association.* The Australian Standards [*AS 1957, 2392, and 2622*] set out words, phrases and cleaning symbols to be used by the manufacturer.

If the manufacturer has consumer interests at heart, then any special care instructions are also given on the label.

Activity 6:5

(1) Make a list of the type of information found on clothing labels that helps you take care of your clothes.
(2) Why should a label showing how to care for a piece of clothing be sewn to it?
(3) Design a label for a school shirt. Take into account all the features that you think are important for wear, including fibre types and washing instructions.

Fig. 6.9 Labels

New fibres and fabrics

The best way to keep out the cold and allow the body to maintain its warm temperature, is to wear many layers of clothing. This can become very uncomfortable and restrict body movement, so manufacturers have invented new types of *thermal* inserts or soft *wadding* for their winter parkas.

There are many new types of fibres and fabrics developed for use in clothing today which have special purposes. *Gore-Tex* and *Thinsulate* are both brand names for fabrics which are used for making parkas and gloves. Gore-Tex is a waterproof fabric which allows water vapour from the body to escape, yet does not allow water to pass into the fabric. Thinsulate is a thermal insulation which was developed by the 3M company to provide *insulation* for cold-climate clothing without adding extra weight to the wearer.

Fig. 6.10 Ski glove label

Fig. 6.11 Ski gloves

Baritherm is a new type of padding used by parka manufacturers which has a much higher thermal value than wadding such as down. The idea is to cut down on the weight of the parka, but not the warmth provided by wadding. The loose nature of the fibre wad creates an airspace which acts as an insulator to the cold outside air.

Fig. 6.12 Parkas

Caring for your clothes

Washing

Because of the different properties various fibres have, not all fabrics can be treated in the same way. Delicate articles may have to be washed by hand, while others may be washed in a machine. Some dyes may run in the wash. It is always best to wash a new garment by itself first to see if the dye comes out in the washing water. Woollen articles that have not been *pre-shrunk* may shrink unless washed in warm water without a strong detergent. Some fabrics do not spin dry well, so check the washing instructions for the '*drip dry*', or '*do not wring or spin*' instruction before washing.

There are different washing cycles on most washing machines now which allow you to choose the length of cycle, water temperature, and spin-dry speed (Fig. 6.13a). This makes it even more difficult at times to decide which is the best cycle for your needs. *More decisions*!

Fig. 6.13a Washing machine showing the different cycle controls

Fig. 6.13b Some synthetic garments may stretch during prolonged washing, and unshrinkproofed wool garments may shrink.

Activity 6:6

(1) Make a list of all the things you have to think about before laundering a brand new garment.
(2) What would be the best way to clean a polyester and cotton school shirt?

Dry-cleaning

What makes a garment dry-cleanable only, and others not dry-cleanable? The labels in Fig. 6.14 will give you some clues.

Fig. 6.14 Fabric labels

Some fibres such as leather and wool are cleaned without damage by the dry-cleaning process. Some garments will look better after dry-cleaning rather than washing, such as coats, pleated skirts, and jackets. Dry-cleaning uses spirits such as *perchloroethylene* to clean clothes rather than water.

Fig. 6.15 Dry-cleaning fluid

Activity 6:7

(1) As a wise consumer, what would you consider before you took a garment to the dry-cleaner's rather than washing it yourself?

(2) Find a garment at home with the label 'Dry-clean Only'. Why do you think the manufacturer has stated this?

(3) Go on an excursion to your local dry-cleaner's to watch the process in action.

Words to remember

goods
services
fibre
yarn
fabric
Baritherm
Goretex
Thinsulate
perchloroethylene

Glossary

Australian Standards Association — This Association prepares and publishes Australian Standards and promotes their adoption. They are prepared by committees which take into account manufacturing capabilities and production efficiency in conjunction with the user's needs.

Thermal — Relating to heat or temperature.

Wadding — A soft bundle of fibres for stuffing or padding.

Insulation — Material that will keep warmth in and cold out.

Activity 6:7 — Revision

(1) **Skill test**:

Answer (a), (b), (c) or (d) to the following questions:

(i) An example of a *good* is:
  (a) a hamburger
  (b) a visit to the doctor
  (c) garbage disposal
  (d) electricity

(ii) An example of a *service* is a:
  (a) shirt
  (b) telephone
  (c) book
  (d) garbage bag

(iii) The *Consumer Affairs Bureau* does not:
  (a) act on behalf of consumers
  (b) provide a service to consumers
  (c) check new products for safety
  (d) set standards for manufacturers to adhere to

(iv) A purchased garment should have:
  (a) a swing tag
  (b) a swing tag and label sewn in to the clothing
  (c) a label sewn into the clothing
  (d) none of the above

Fig. 6.16 Care label

(v) The label in Fig. 6.16 should not be:
- (a) machine washed
- (b) hand washed
- (c) bleached
- (d) ironed

(vi) A new waterproof fabric is called:
- (a) Baritherm
- (b) Gore-Tex
- (c) Thinsulate
- (d) Polyester

(2) **What am I?**
My first letter is in *fabric* but never in *fibre*
My second letter is in *goods* and also in *perchloroethylene*
My third letter is in *yarn* and also in *Thinsulate*
My fourth letter is in *services* but never in *Baritherm*
My fifth letter is in *insulation* but never in *wadding*
My sixth letter is in *Baritherm* but never in *fibre*
My seventh letter is in *thermal* and also in *fibre*
My last letter is in *Goretex* and also in *yarn*
What am I?

(3) (a) **Unscramble the letters to find words that have been used in this chapter**.
AMEHLTR
VCEISRES
ISLETUHNTA
INSGPOPH
DNIDAWG
IEBFR

(b) Write down the letters in the circles and then unscramble the letters to complete this sentence:
Insulation can be bulky without adding extra _ _ _ _ _ _ to the garment.

Further reading

Brideoake, O. and Grosset, J., *What to Wear*, Longman Cheshire, Melbourne, 1977
Wellings, H., *Buying Power*, Edward Arnold, Melbourne, 1982

Addresses for further information and assignments

The Australian Standards Association [Head Office]
PO Box 458
North Sydney NSW 2060

The Consumer Affairs Bureau [Head Office]
Consumer Claims Tribunal
GPO Box 468
Sydney NSW 2001

or Check the phone book for the address in your state.

7

Clothing and you

Fig. 7.1 Different shops

The clothes people decide to buy are purchased after many influences have been considered. Sometimes we are aware of these influences and at other times we are not.

Advertising

Advertising on the radio, television and in magazines encourages us to buy clothes. Sometimes we do not need the clothes we decide to buy but the advertising has made us feel we need them.

Money

The money we have to spend is a resource that is limited. Therefore, it is necessary to plan what we want to spend it on. Money will influence what shops we purchase clothes from and the style of clothing we buy. Very *fashionable* clothing is expensive and goes out of date quickly. People often purchase clothes that are not too fashionable so they can get value for money. In such cases, clothes can be worn longer.

Shops

Some people will buy clothes because they like them or they are on sale. This is known as impulse buying and can be a waste of money.

To prevent wasting your money, plan what clothes you need and where you will buy them. Some shops sell the same or similar clothes at different prices. The price may vary because:

- One style is more fashionable.
- The fabric of one may be better quality.
- Shops sell the same item for different prices.

Activity 7:1

(1) Make a list of all the shops at which you would purchase clothes.
Some of these shops may be department stores selling more than just clothes and others may specialise in one item of clothes such as jeans, while a third group may sell a range of clothes.

(2) In 3 to 4 sentences explain the types of clothes the shops sell and the differences you would expect in the price.

Activity 7:2 — Survey

Pete decided to buy a pair of basic blue denim jeans. He wants value for money so would like to shop around and compare the prices.

In your workbook, complete the following chart for Pete. Go to four different shops.

Shop	Brand	Jeans style: brief description	Suggested care of jeans	Price
1. 2. 3. 4.				

(1) Which shop was the cheapest?
(2) Did all the jeans suggest the same method of cleaning?
(3) Which jeans suggested different cleaning methods. Can you suggest why this is so?
(4) Was there a price difference between brands?
(5) Did the one brand cost different amounts in the various shops?
(6) Give reasons why the price of jeans varies.
(7) What jeans would you suggest Pete buys? Give reasons.

What size are you?

No one is exactly the same size as anyone else. So that patterns and clothing can be sold, standard measurements have been developed. Body measurements indicate the size of your body. To measure your body where you have been instructed by your teacher, hold the tape measure so it is comfortably snug but not tight.

Record your measurements.

Activity 7:3

Copy the chart into your workbook and record your measurements. These will need to be checked regularly as measurements change as you grow or put on weight.

<table>
<tr><th>Her measurements</th><th>Your measurements</th><th>Date</th><th colspan="2">Her pattern size</th></tr>
<tr><td>Bust</td><td></td><td></td><td>Dress/ blouse</td><td></td></tr>
<tr><td>Waist</td><td></td><td></td><td rowspan="3">Skirt/pants</td><td rowspan="3"></td></tr>
<tr><td>Hips</td><td></td><td></td></tr>
<tr><td>Back waist length</td><td></td><td></td></tr>
</table>

<table>
<tr><th>His measurements</th><th>Your measurements</th><th>Date</th><th colspan="2">His pattern size</th></tr>
<tr><td>Chest</td><td></td><td></td><td rowspan="4">Shirt/ jacket</td><td rowspan="4"></td></tr>
<tr><td>Waist</td><td></td><td></td></tr>
<tr><td>Hips (seat)</td><td></td><td></td></tr>
<tr><td>Shirt neck — neck + 13 mm</td><td></td><td></td></tr>
<tr><td>Shirt sleeve</td><td></td><td></td><td rowspan="4">Pants</td><td rowspan="4"></td></tr>
<tr><td>Height</td><td></td><td></td></tr>
<tr><td>Trouser length</td><td></td><td></td></tr>
<tr><td>Inseam length</td><td></td><td></td></tr>
</table>

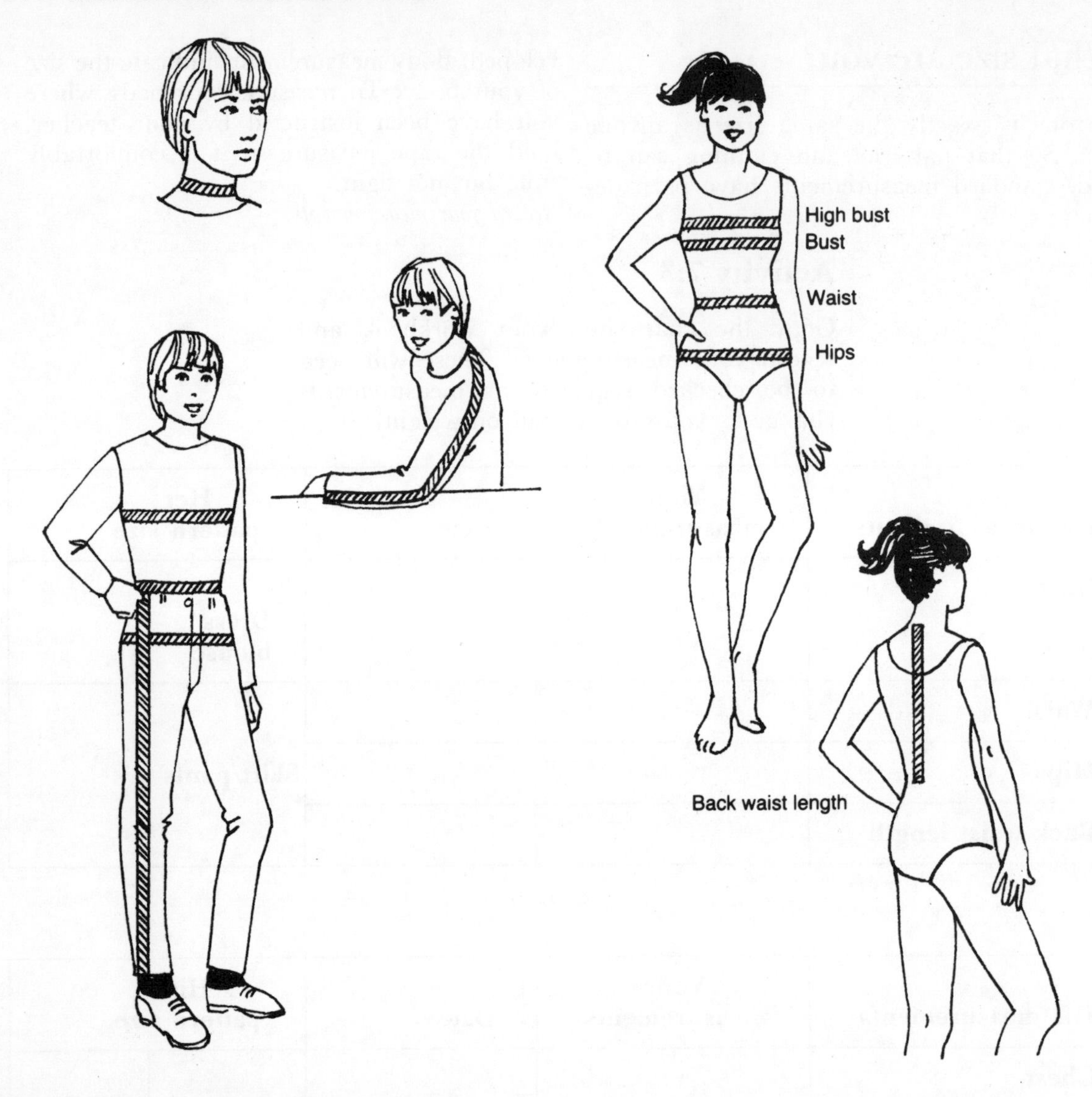

Fig. 7.2 How to measure males and females

Girls' and women's measurements

Misses' Size	6	8	10	12	14	16	18	20	
Bust	78	80	83	87	92	97	102	107	cm
Waist	58	61	64	67	71	76	81	87	cm
Hip	83	85	88	92	97	102	107	112	cm
Back waist Length	39.5	40	40.5	41.5	42	42.5	43	44	cm

Young junior/teen Size	5/6	7/8	9/10	11/12	13/14	15/16	
Bust	71	74	78	81	85	89	cm
Waist	56	58	61	64	66	69	cm
Hip	79	81	85	89	93	97	cm
Back waist Length	34.5	35.5	37	38	39	40	cm

Women's Size	38	40	42	44	46	48	50	
Bust	107	112	117	122	127	132	137	cm
Waist	89	94	99	105	112	118	124	cm
Hip	112	117	122	127	132	137	142	cm
Back waist Length	44	44	44.5	45	45	45.5	46	cm

Half-size Size	10½	12½	14½	16½	18½	20½	22½	24½	
Bust	84	89	94	99	104	109	114	119	cm
Waist	69	74	79	84	89	96	102	108	cm
Hip	89	94	99	104	109	116	122	128	cm
Back waist Length	38	39	39.5	40	40.5	40.5	41	41.5	cm

	Boys'				Teen-Boys'				
Size	7	8	10	12	14	16	18	20	
Chest	66	69	71	76	81	85	89	93	cm
Waist	58	61	64	66	69	71	74	76	cm
Hip (seat)	69	71	75	79	83	87	90	94	cm
Shirt neck size	30	31	32	33	34.5	35.5	37	38	cm
Height	122	127	137	147	155	163	168	173	cm

Men's Size	34	36	38	40	42	44	46	48	
Chest	87	92	97	102	107	112	117	122	cm
Waist	71	76	81	87	92	99	107	112	cm
Hip (seat)	89	94	99	104	109	114	119	124	cm
Shirt neck size	35.5	37	38	39.5	40.5	42	43	44.5	cm
Shirt sleeve	81	81	84	84	87	87	89	89	cm

Today a large variety of fabrics exists from which people can select to suit their needs. Being a wise consumer means thinking about why you are buying fabric, that is, what it is going to be used for.

What performance could each of the people in Fig. 7.2 expect from their clothes?

The way a fabric will perform depends on the *fibres* in the fabric as well as the way it is made. Most fabric used for clothes is *woven* or *knitted*.

Conduct these simple tests to tell you about the fabric. This will help you to make a wise choice.

Remember

- Know what you want the fabric for.
- Estimate how much money can be spent on the fabric.
- Generally the roll of fabric has a label attached that has the fibre content and a brief description of how to care for the fabric. Read this label as it will help you to decide whether the fabric is suitable for your needs.

Fig. 7.3 Clothes for different needs

Consumer checklist

The following tests will help you to make a wise decision.

Activity 7:4 — How will the fabric drape?

Drape is the way fabric falls in folds.

(1) Obtain a variety of fabrics from your school scrap-box.
(2) Place the fabric, one piece at a time, over your arm. Gather the fabric up with the other hand and hold it *draped* over your arm.
(3) Look carefully at the number of folds that have occurred.

Each fabric that you have selected will have a different number of folds. Each fabric has a different drape and is therefore suitable for some clothes and not others.

Activity 7:5 — Will the fabric crease?

Some fabrics *crease* badly while other crease very little.

(1) Crush the fabric in your hand for a few seconds, then release it.
(2) Write down your results.

The amount a fabric will crease depends on the fibres in the fabric and the way the fabric is woven. Each fibre has its own characteristics — some fabrics that are used a lot by consumers are:

- *Cotton* — creases easily
- *Linen* — creases a lot
- *Wool* — generally does not get bad creases
- *Polyester* — does not crease very much
- *Nylon* — does not crease very much

Some creases are easily removed by ironing while others will come out overnight if the item is hung carefully on a coat hanger.

Activity 7:6 — Is the fabric safe?

There are many fabrics that can be bought in shops that are not safe for you to wear. This is because they may burn quickly or melt. In both cases if the fabric was made into clothing, the wearer could be badly burnt in the case of an accident.

(1) As a class, obtain a sample of each fabric that has been tested.
(2) Ask you teacher to burn each sample.
Note: This should be done over a metal tray **by your teacher** so no damage is done to furnishings.
(3) Record your results.

How a fabric burns is very important to the consumer. This is especially the case with nightwear because many fabrics such as nylon melt and cotton flannelette burns quickly. *Legislation* has been brought in to help stop children getting burnt. Labels on clothes and clothing styles have been improved.

A consumer must carefully check that the fabric suits the article they wish to make. Further testing can be carried out on fabrics in the shop.

On buying the fabric, other tests can be done. These can help the consumer to get the best out of the constructed article.

Three tests to complete would include:

- *Washability* — Cut a sample of fabric and wash in the way clothes are usually washed in your family.

  Report your findings. Perhaps this method is suitable but sometimes fabrics need special care. Maybe a cold water wash or dry-cleaning needs to be considered.

- *Attracting dirt* — Some fabrics attract more dirt than others. The amount of static electricity a fabric builds up will affect this.
- *Ironing temperature* — When the fabric has a label indicating what it is made of, set the iron at that temperature. When the fibre content in the fabric is not known, start ironing at the lowest temperature until the most suitable ironing setting is reached. Note this setting.

Caring for your clothes

To ensure that your clothes last the length of time expected, care must be taken that is suitable to the garment.

Read the label

When deciding to buy clothing, look at the label sewn into the garment. This label will explain how to care for the garment and if you want your garment to last, you need to follow these instructions.

Sometimes a clothing label will say '*Dry-clean Only*'. It is important to remember that each time clothing is dry-cleaned it will cost money that could end up making the item very expensive.

Because clothing from one country is often sold all over the world an *international textile care labelling code* has been developed. Based on symbols, it does not cause problems with people who speak different languages. While it is being used, it has yet to be fully accepted by all manufacturers.

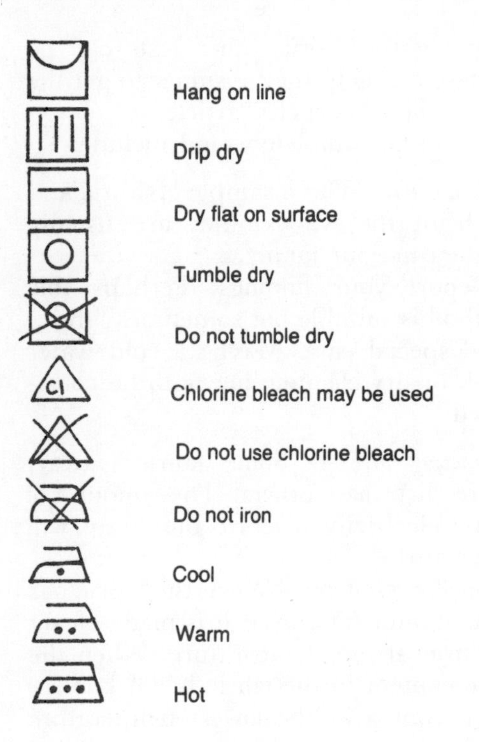

Fig. 7.4 Care symbols

The International Wool Secretariat has developed symbols as well. Wool, a natural fibre obtained from sheep, is expensive when compared to man-made fibres.

However, wool is a very warm, elastic fibre with many advantages for the consumer. The label makes it easy for the consumer to identify.

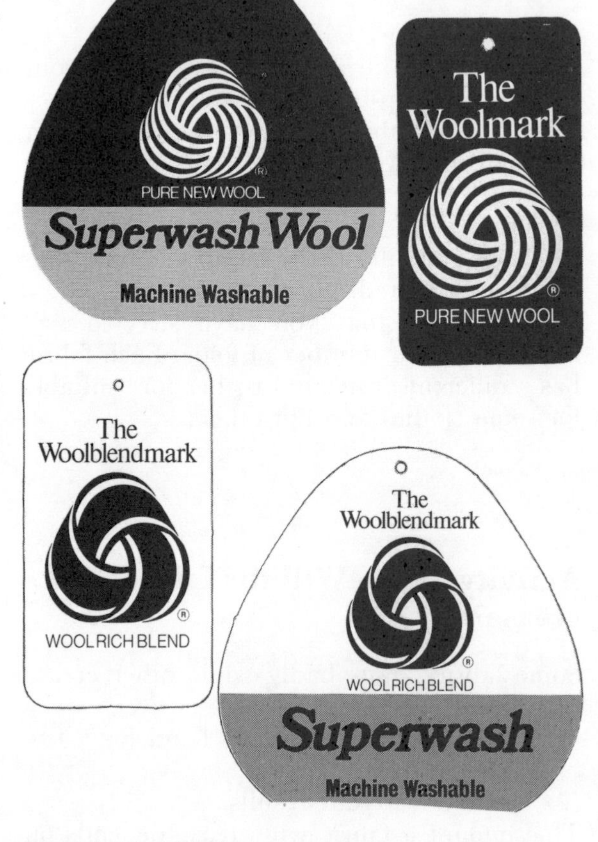

Fig. 7.5 Wool labels

Bright as new

Automatic washing machines make cleaning clothes very easy today.

Because of the wide variety of fabrics, some have special needs. Fabrics made from synthetic fibres develop a lot of static electricity that causes the clothing to cling to the wearer. *Fabric conditioners* such as Comfort remove the static and make clothes more comfortable to wear.

A wide variety of fabric detergents are available.

- *Soap powders* — Some fabrics do not wash well in soap. It does not wash clothes well in hard water.
- *Synthetic washing powders* — These products form a good lather even in hard water.
- *Biological powders* — These break down protein and are very good for soaking nappies and blood stained items.
- *Crease solvent powders* — These get greasy marks out of clothes.

Spotless

From time to time we spill something on our clothes. A stain may result that ruins or spoils the garment. This chart gives quick remedies for simple stains.

For many busy people the pre-wash spray-on stain removers are quick and easy. However, some stains require another method of treatment.

Stain	**Treatment**
Protein stains, e.g. egg, blood, milk	Wash in cool water and enzyme wash powder.
Grass and ball point ink	Apply methylated spirits and wash.
Mildew	Use bleach carefully on affected areas and then rinse immediately. Do not use on coloured fabrics as it also removes the colour.
Grease, shoe polish, make-up	Use a grease solvent powder.
Chewing gum	Remove as much as possible and then use a grease solvent to remove the stain.
Paint	Use turps, a paint solvent. Use it as quickly as possible before the stain sets.

Planning your image

The clothes you buy project an image of the type of person you are.

When planning to buy clothes consider:

- The activities you are involved in.
- The colours you feel comfortable wearing.
- Which clothes are suitable for the climate.
- Choosing easy care fabrics that can be easily washed.
- Selecting outfits with two or three parts so you can co-ordinate (mix and match).

Ready made versus making your own

Advantages **Ready made**	**Made myself**
• Try it on before you buy. • Sometimes can be altered to fit. • Wear it straight away.	• Costs less. • Make the item to fit. • Select both fabric and and style. • Pleasant leisure-time activity.
Disadvantages • More expensive. • Mass produced. Other people have same item.	• Not all designs are simple to make. • Your time is also a cost to you.

Activity 7:7 — Case study

During the Christmas break you will be going to the beach for a two-week holiday. So you can buy the clothes you will need, $200 was given to you as a Christmas present.

(1) Make a list of all the clothes needed for the holiday. Remember, you will already have some clothes.

(2) Having decided what is needed, go to the shops and look around. Compare the prices of items needed in two shops.

Clothes needed	Shop 1		Shop 2	
	Item	Price	Item	Price

(3) Decide where you will buy each item. Sometimes you will select the more expensive item because it is better value.

(4) Did you have enough money to buy the clothing? If not, what could you do to get better value for your money?

Words to remember

advertising
fashionable
denim
woven
knitted
drape
mildew
crease
cotton
wool
polyester
legislation
washability
co-ordinate
label
international
conditioners
synthetic
biological
solvent
grease

Activity 7:8 — Revision

(1) Find the following words in the wonderword.

clothing	money	woven	crease	burn	dirt
purchase	cotton	damage	static	jeans	iron
influence	choice	linen	fabric	drape	advertising
consumer	wool	labels	garment	gather	nylon
wash	textile	legislation		stains	gum
paint					

C	L	O	T	H	I	N	G	P	U	R	C	H	A	S	E	B	E
O	H	W	L	I	N	E	N	F	O	R	O	E	D	B	U	F	Y
N	I	O	N	G	F	L	P	A	I	N	T	C	V	L	O	A	T
S	Y	O	I	H	L	E	E	S	G	A	T	H	E	R	A	B	W
U	N	L	I	C	U	I	L	S	E	C	O	O	R	N	S	R	U
M	M	A	O	E	E	S	A	B	U	R	N	S	T	A	T	I	C
E	R	I	E	N	N	U	B	S	A	S	T	A	I	N	S	C	W
R	A	R	E	J	C	R	E	A	S	E	O	T	S	R	F	T	H
M	D	R	A	P	E	E	L	E	A	P	R	P	I	A	O	R	E
U	N	E	V	O	W	A	S	H	L	I	M	O	N	E	Y	N	N
G	A	R	M	E	N	T	E	E	D	A	M	A	G	E	D	E	D
L	E	G	I	S	L	A	T	I	O	N	T	E	X	T	I	L	E

Note: Some words are written backwards.

(2) Use the left-over letters to fill in the blanks to make a sentence.

_ _ _ _ _ _   _ _ _ _ _ _   _ _ _ _ _ _ _
_   _ _ _ _ _ _ _ _ _ _ _ _ _   _ _
_ _ _ _ _   _ _   _ _ _   _ _ _ _ _ _ _
_ _ _ _ _ _.

(3) Choose words from the list above to complete the following sentences. Write the complete sentences in your book.

(a) ________ encourages us to buy clothing by making us aware of the variety of clothing available.

(b) As a ________ you need to select clothing wisely to get the best *value for money*.

(c) Most fabric people buy is either ________ or ________. Collect a sample of each and paste into your book.

(d) If a fabric has many folds, it is said to have good ________.

(e) ________ creases easily, but ________ will crease a lot more. Both these fibres will need ironing with a hot iron.

(f) ________ generally does not crease easily. Careful hanging on a coat hanger at night will reduce the number of creases.

(g) A ________ indicates how to care for an item of clothing.

(h) Quick attention to a ________ on clothes means it is more likely to be removed.

(4) The following words have been used in the chapter. Use each word in a sentence to show you understand the meaning. If you are not sure, go back through the chapter and read the paragraph with the word in it again.

- legislation
- leisure
- mildew
- burn
- fashionable

8

Clothing shapes

Production of clothing

In *medieval* times, it was the duty of a wife to provide clothing for her family and servants. The fibres used to make clothes were generally wool or flax. These fibres were spun into yarn in the home. Professional weavers made the yarn into cloth and tailors made the clothes for the men and women who could afford them. If people were poor, the wife would cut the pattern for the clothes and sew them herself.

Until the last 100 years, simple everyday clothes and underclothes were made at home. These clothes would have been sewn completely by hand. Clothing styles changed very little. Clothes were made by making a pattern from an existing garment. Because silk and velvet were expensive, clothes made from these fabrics were not thrown away. People either made them into clothes for children or trimmed them with new fabric.

About 300 years ago, women set up establishments to make clothes. Such a woman was known as a sempstress (or seamstress) and had professional status. Clothes made would have included men's shirts, cuffs and cravats and dress accessories for ladies.

By the middle of the nineteenth century, clothing production had changed. People had more money to spend on clothing and they wanted to wear more fashionable clothes. In England, shops were selling a range of goods and the start of the department store was evident. Magazines mainly concerned with fashion were being published. Paper patterns now refered to as commercial patterns were being sold.

Activity 8:1

(1) Look closely at the jacket worn by the Victorian lady.
 (a) Where would such a jacket be worn?
 (b) How comfortable do you think the jacket would be? Give reasons for your decision.

(2) Collect commercial patterns from your family or neighbours that were used to make clothes over 20 years ago.
 (a) Find out the year they were used.
 (b) Bring the patterns to school and compare the styles with patterns other students have collected.
 (c) In your workbook draw two of the pattern styles.
 (d) Write down the main differences you see in patterns of yesterday compared with patterns of today.
 (e) Write down at least one reason why patterns are different. Discuss this with class members.

Buying patterns today

Today people buy patterns to make clothes and a variety of other articles such as bean bags and household articles. Patterns are purchased from *haberdashery* sections of large department stores or fabric shops where

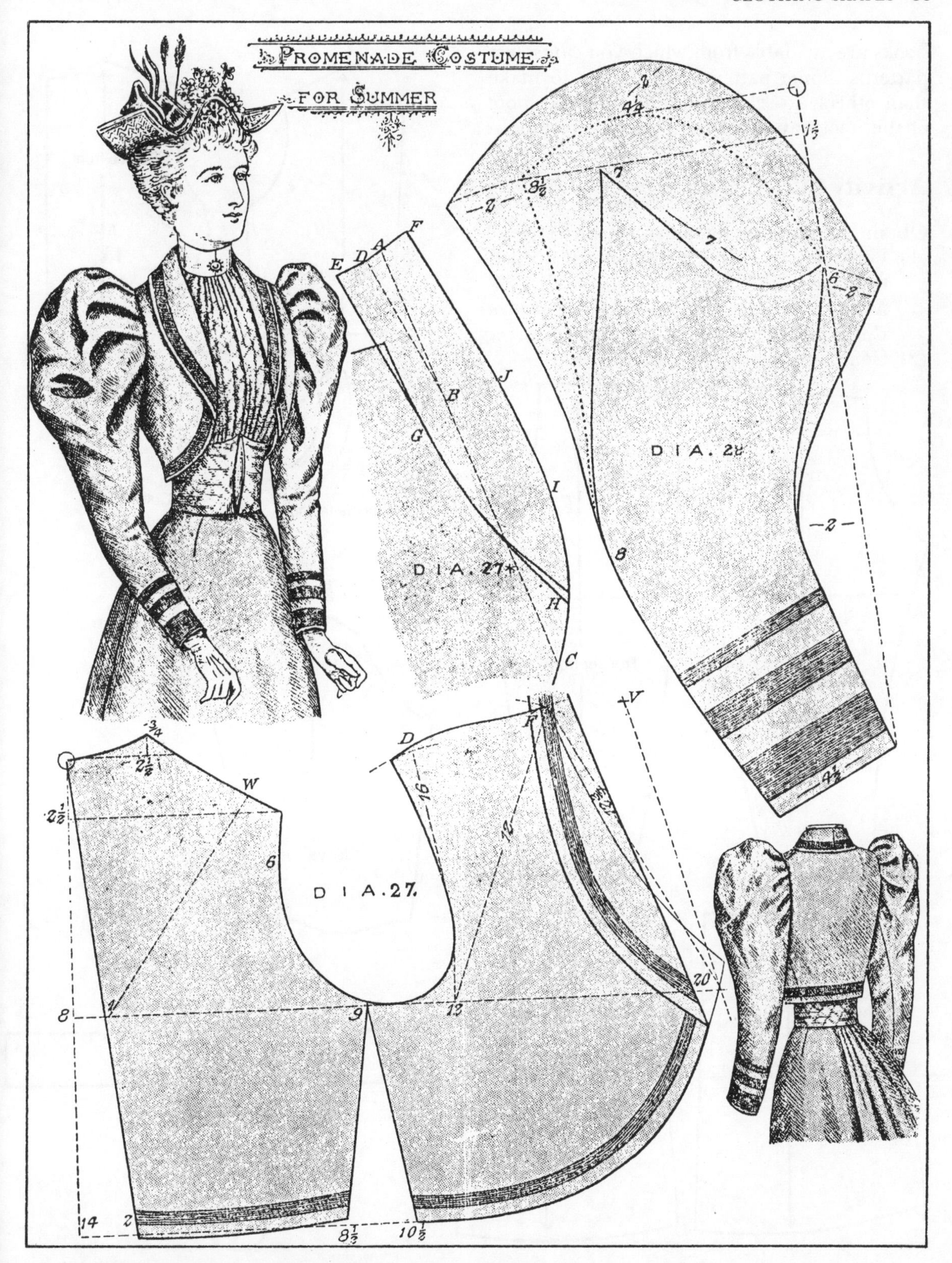

Fig. 8.1 Pattern for a Victorian lady's jacket

books are available from which you can select patterns. Some patterns are harder to make than others, so select carefully and take note of the information on the pattern envelope.

Activity 8:2

Obtain six patterns for different shirt styles.
(1) Look closely at the tissue pattern needed to make each shirt.
Note: Each style will have *different pattern shapes* but there are many similarities.
(2) Compile a list of the similarities.

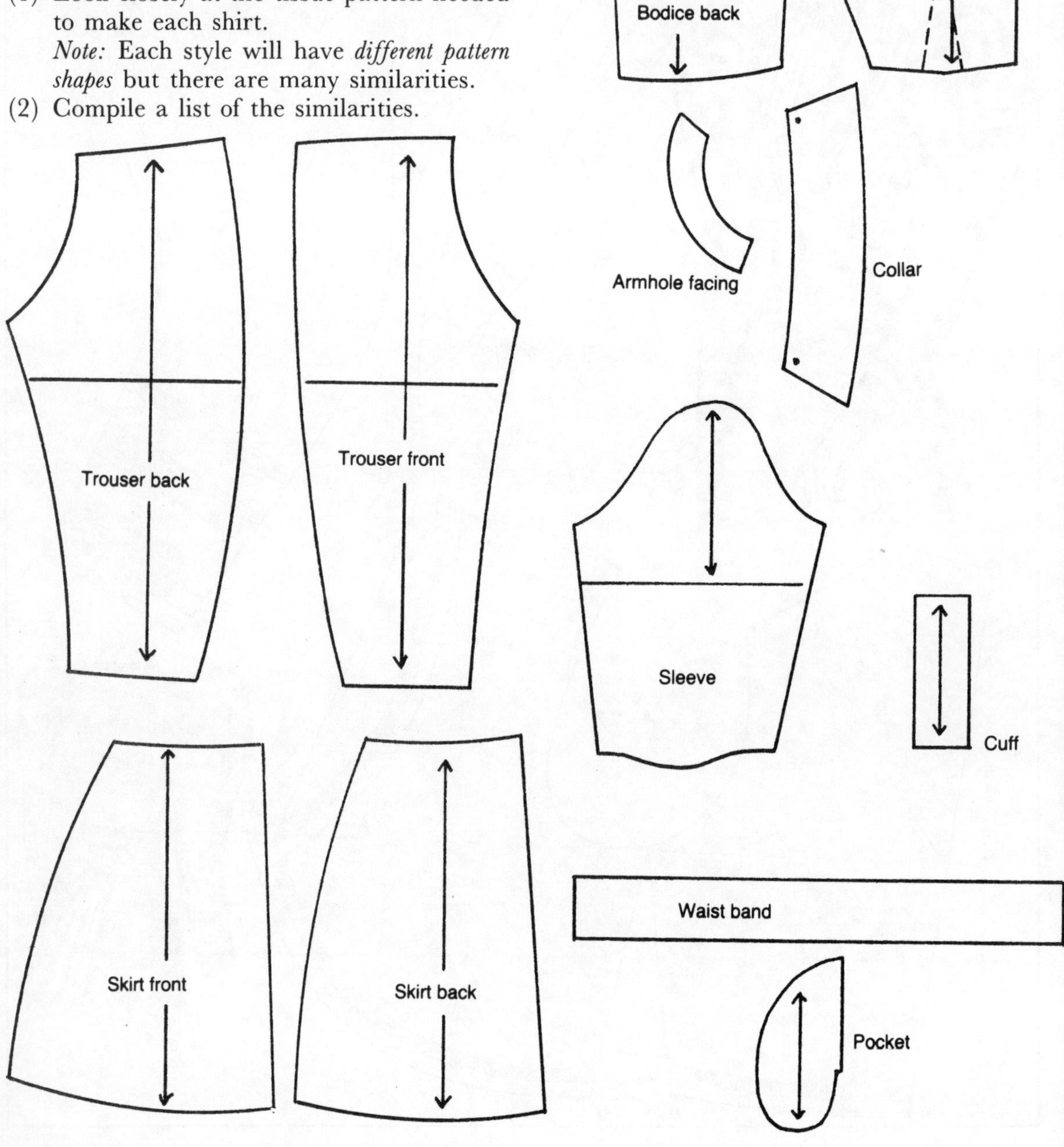

Fig. 8.3 Basic pattern shapes

Basic pattern shapes

Illustrated in Fig. 8.3 are the *basic pattern shapes*.

From the basic pattern shapes any style of clothing can be made. The basic style includes:

Bodice front and back — Blouses, shirts and the top section of dresses are made from this. On the front bodice illustrated are dotted lines. These dotted lines show where extra fabric has been added to give shape to the front. When you begin sewing, the dots are joined to make *darts* which give shape and fit. Darts are mainly used with woven fabrics because they do not mould as easily as knit fabrics to the shape of the body.

To neaten the armhole, a facing is used. However, when you put sleeves in, the facing is no longer needed.

To finish the neckline, a collar may be used. Collars come in different shapes and sizes as shown in Fig. 8.4 and have been given different names so they are easily identified.

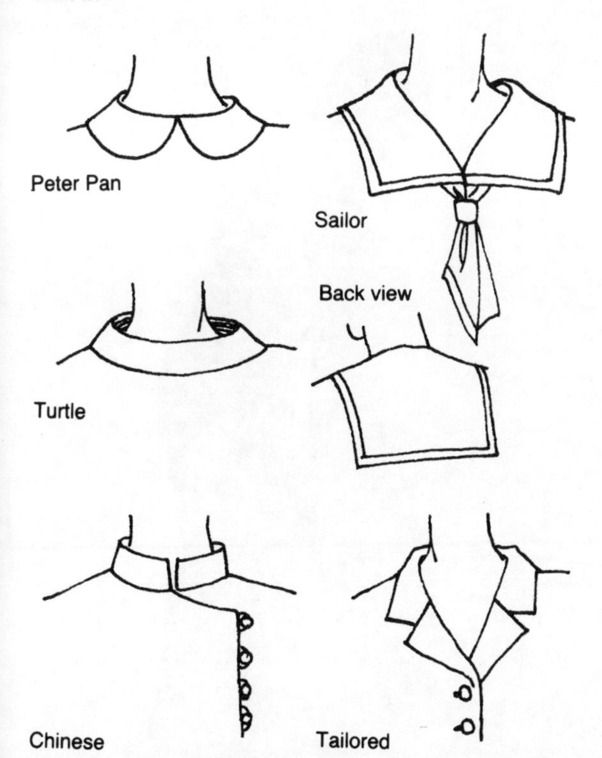

Fig. 8.4 Collars and their shapes

The Sleeve — The sleeve shown is a long one that is gathered into a cuff. Sleeves are available in different styles. To make a short sleeve, the pattern is cut in half along the horizontal line.

The Skirt — The skirt pattern in Fig. 8.5 is fitted and forms a basic shape that fits the shape of the body. Other skirt designs can be adapted from this basic skirt shape.

The Trousers — From the basic trouser pattern in Fig. 8.5 styles are designed to suit current fashion trends. Shorts can be made by cutting the pattern in half along the horizontal line. Depending on the style, both trousers and skirts will require a waistband and pockets.

Fig. 8.5 Articles of clothing designed from the basic block patterns

Activity 8:3

1. Identify which pattern pieces are needed to construct the different items. Match the patterns and styles shown in Fig. 8.6.

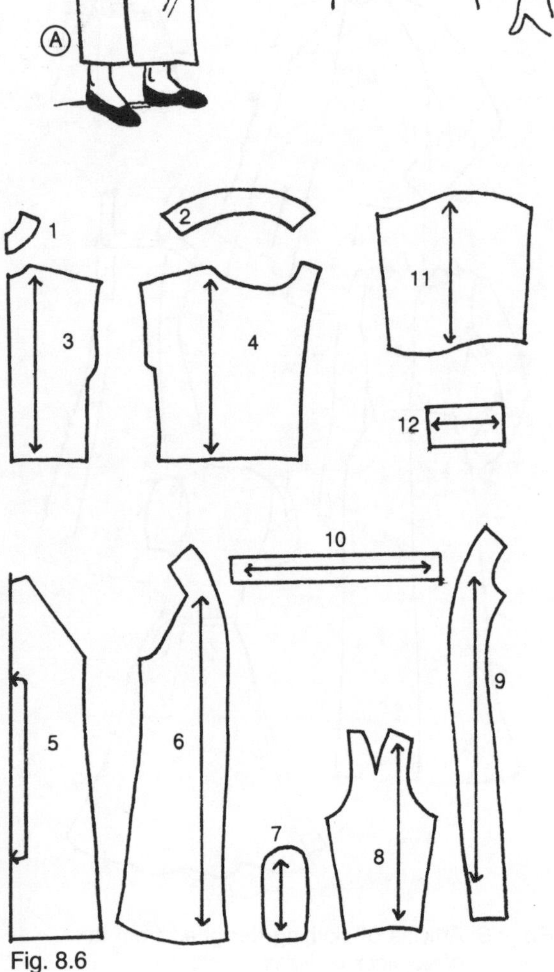

Fig. 8.6

Remember that pattern pieces should be kept in *proportion*. This means, for example, that a collar or facing pattern should always be smaller than the shirt.

By comparing pattern envelopes from different years you can see how styles have changed.

Fig. 8.7 Two styles of children's clothing

2. Compare the two styles in Fig. 8.7 then answer these questions.
   (a) Who would be able to run around and play the most? Why?
   (b) What clothes would need most care? (Write 2 to 4 sentences.)
   (c) Can you tell who is the boy and who is the girl?

Fashion cycles

It is believed by many that the style of clothes goes in cycles. For example, the fashions people wear today are an adaptation of what people wore many years ago. The changes in style occur for a number of reasons:

- No one wants to wear exactly the same styles as their great grandparents and who would wear the same clothes as their parents?
- People want to be a little individual or different in the clothes they wear. As teenagers though, people tend to wear the same as other people the same age. Have you ever telephoned a friend to find out what they are wearing to a school dance?

Today fashion changes very quickly

In one season, such as summer, more than one fashion style or trend can be seen. A number of reasons can be given for these changes.

- We are influenced by designers from all over the world.
- People travel a lot more.
  a) People travel overseas.
  b) Fashion trends from overseas are brought back home.
- People have more money to spend on clothes.
- Mass production has made clothes cheaper and easier to obtain.
- People do many activities and need clothing for school, sport, work and going out. Casual and 'good' clothes are needed for specific occasions.

Fig. 8.8 Clothes for specific occasions

Identify the different occasions in Fig. 8.8 and list the clothes the people are wearing. To take part in all these activities a large variety of clothes would be needed.
The consumer has an influence on clothing styles and a style will only be successful if the consumer buys it. If a style is popular it may last for a few seasons. Some styles are referred to as *fad* fashions and are only worn for a few months. Clothes that are worn year after year with little change are called *classic* styles.

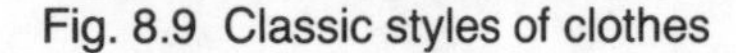

Fig. 8.9 Classic styles of clothes

Classic styles (Fig. 8.9) include such items of clothing as suits for both men and women. The main changes in style may include the method of buttoning the jacket, the style of skirt (it may be straight or pleated) and the width of the trouser legs.

In Australia we have four seasons — autumn, winter, spring and summer. Manufacturers take advantage of this and prepare four ranges of clothes for the consumer to buy.

Fashion success and the consumer

Present-day consumers are well informed and can make better judgements about clothes. Today people can:

- Read magazines.
- Obtain information from consumer associations.

- Read clothing labels.
- Observe advertising and make comparisons.

Activity 8:4 — Pullover top

Fig. 8.10 shows a very loose fitting top suitable to wear at the beach over a swimming costume.

Fig. 8.10 A pullover top

You will need

- 1.25 m of knit fabric, 90 cm wide
- Matching thread
- 0.5 m knitted rib fabric
- Pins and needles
- Equipment to decorate if desired

Method

(1) Make your paper pattern from the scale pattern (Fig. 8.11).
(2) The front and back are the same. The pattern pieces are placed on the fold of the fabric (Fig. 8.12).
(3) Using the measurements, draw the front and back of the top.
(4) *Pattern layout* — place the pattern pieces on the fabric as shown. Seam allowances have been included in the pattern.

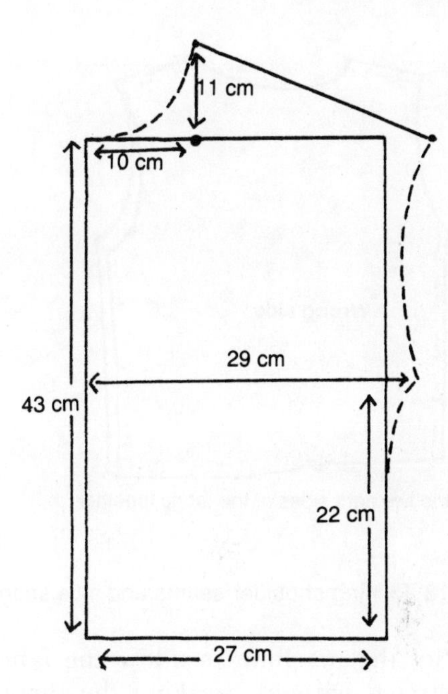

Fig. 8.11 Scale pattern of pullover top

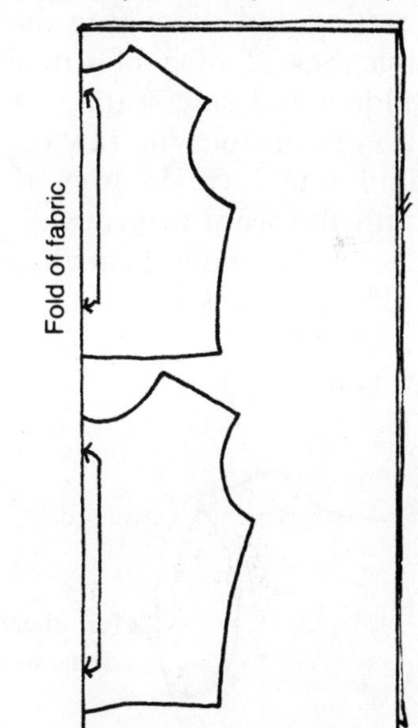

Fig. 8.12 Pattern layout

Note: Often you can buy very wide knit fabric. If this is possible you may be able to pin your pattern pieces side by side and will only need half the meterage of the fabric.

(4) Remove the paper patterns and place the right sides of the front and back together. Pin the shoulder seams and side seams as shown in Fig. 8.13.

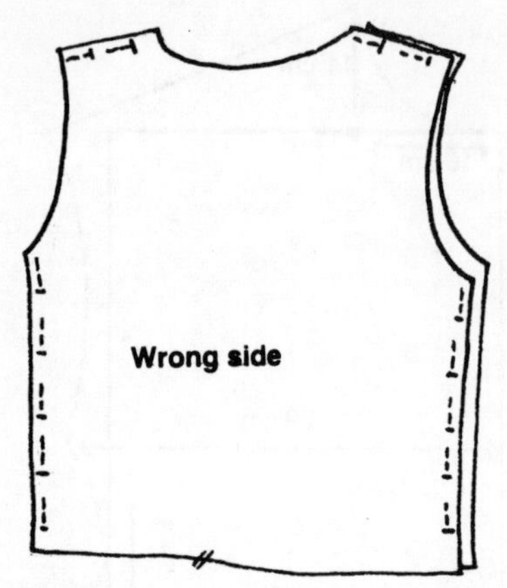

- Put the two right sides of the fabric together.
- Pin.

Fig. 8.13 Pinning shoulder seams and side seams

(5) Set the machine to allow the fabric to stretch without breaking the thread by putting the straight stitch dial on the middle setting and the zigzag dial on a half stitch. Sew 2 rows of stitching on the shoulders and side seams. The first row is 1.5 cm in from the raw edge and the second row 1 cm in from the raw edge. Trim the seam to neaten.

(6) *Armholes* — Turn under 2 cm all the way around. Pin and tack.

(7) Neaten the armholes using 2 rows of stitching (Fig. 8.14).

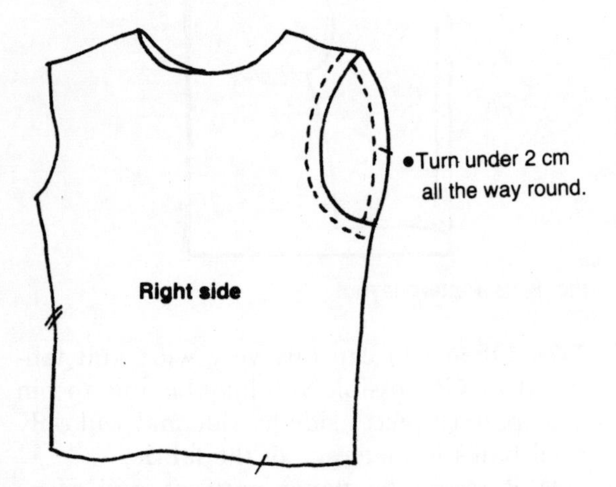

Fig. 8.14 Neatening the armholes

(8) Waistband — Measure around the waist. The waistband is 2/3 the waist measurement plus 12 cm. Join using machine stitching. Fold the waistband in half as shown in Fig. 8.15

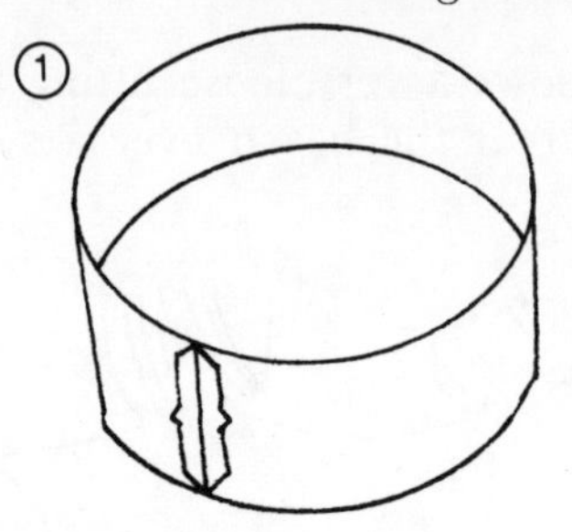

- Machine and press seam open.

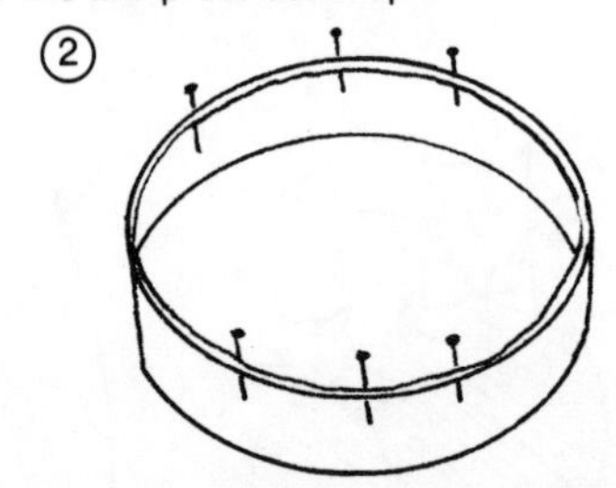

- Fold band in half so that the wrong sides are together and the raw edges even. • Pin.

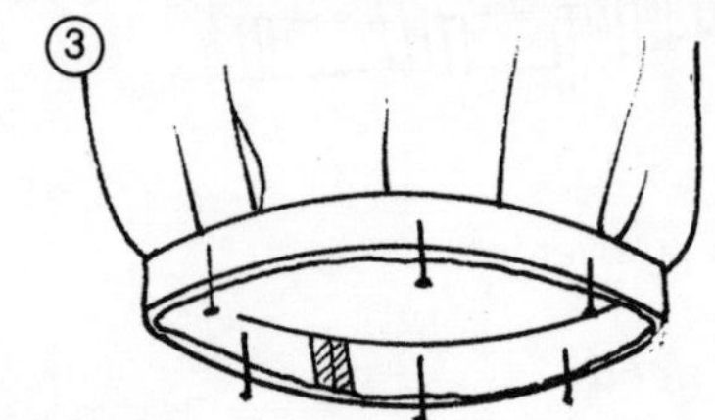

- Stretch band to fit the waist.
- Pin as shown.

Fig. 8.15 Waistband construction

(9) Stretch waistband evenly to fit the bottom of the pullover top, pin, tack, machine and trim fabric.

(10) Zigzag edges together or do another row of stitching to neaten and strengthen.

(11) Neck — The neck can be finished by:
 a) Turning under the same as sleeves
 or
 b) Trimming with ribbing (5 cm wide) using the same method as for the waistband.

(12) Decorate the front if desired with fabric paints or fabric crayons.

Activity 8:5 — Super shirt

Fig. 8.16 Super shirt

One size fits all boys and girls of 11–14 years.

You will need

- 2.5 m of 90 cm wide fabric. Choose a firm fabric such as cotton gaberdine, sail cloth, or calico.
- Thread to match
- 0.3 m of iron-on vilene interfacing

Method

Note: It is important that you press the shirt at every stage of making so that you will be happy with the end result.

(1) Enlarge the pattern diagram (Fig. 8.17) to its correct size.

(2) Lay out fabric and pin on the pattern as shown in Fig. 8.18.

(3) Cut out fabric carefully. Cut one piece of interfacing from the collar pattern.

(4) Press front facings under 3 mm and sew using a straight machine stitch (Fig. 8.19).

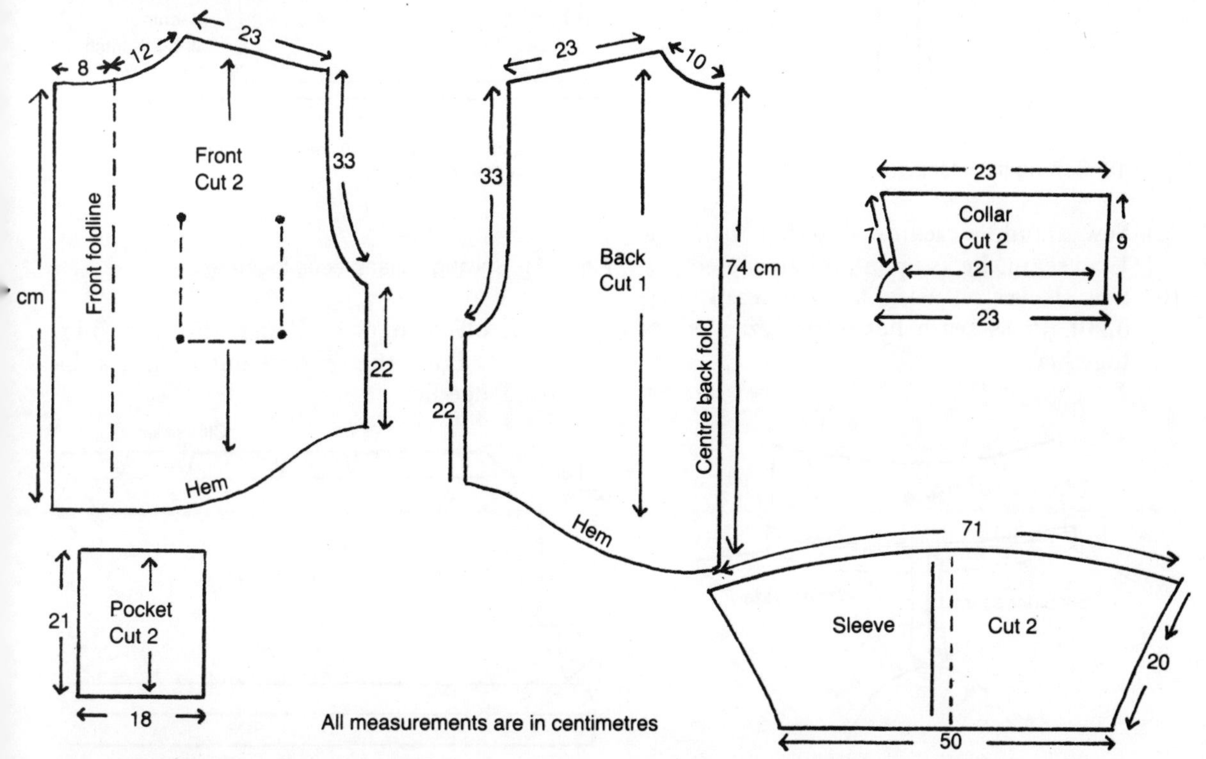

Fig. 8.17 Pattern for shirt

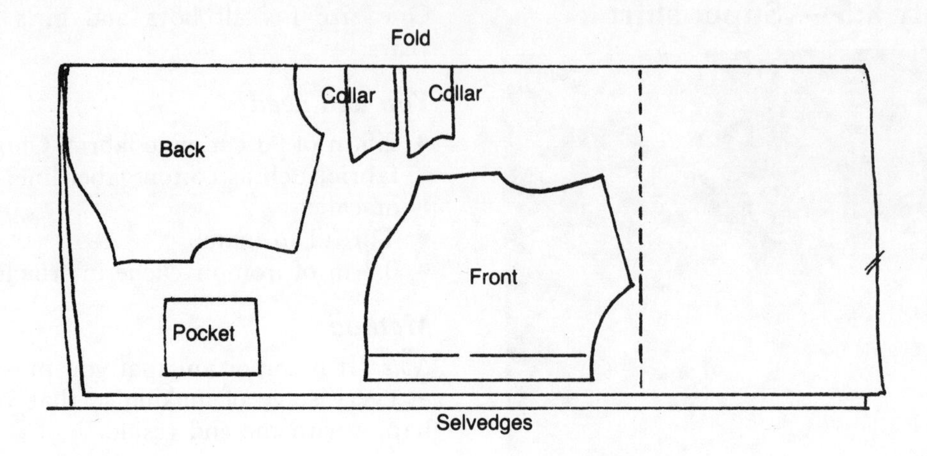

Fig. 8.18 Pattern layout for cutting out

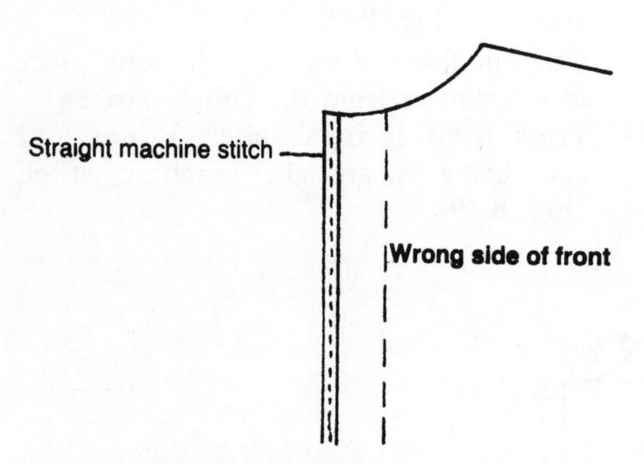

Fig. 8.19 Sewing front facings

(5) Sew shoulder seams together using a 1 cm seam. Press open and zigzag edges.
(6) Sew sleeves on using a 1 cm seam (Fig. 8.20). Press seam flat and zigzag edges together.

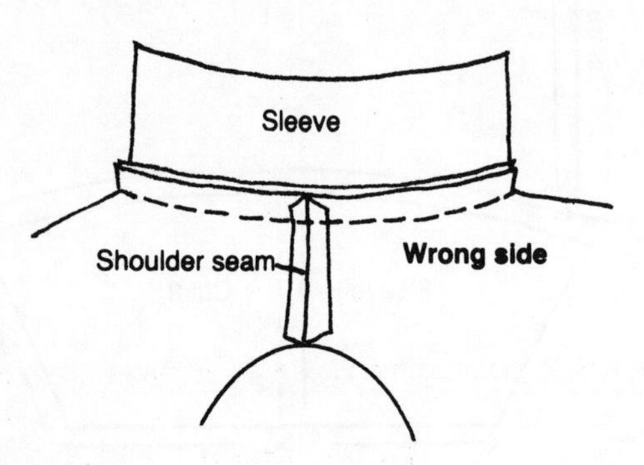

Fig. 8.20 Sewing on the sleeves

(7) Iron interfacing onto the wrong side of one of the collar pieces.
(8) Place collar pieces with right sides together and sew 1 cm from the outside edge (Fig. 8.21).

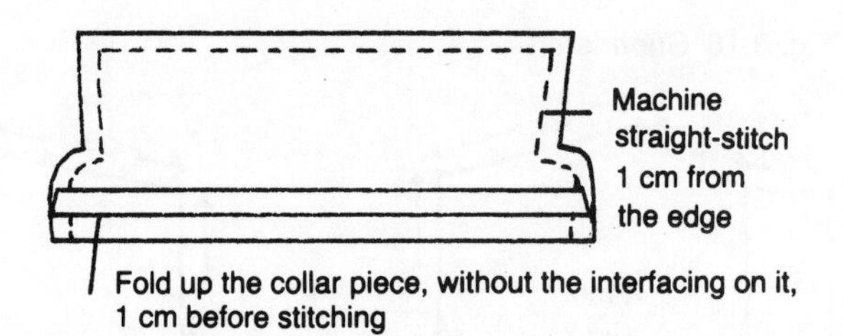

Fig. 8.21 Sewing collar pieces together

(9) Cut off corners and turn through (Fig. 8.22). Push the corners out with a knitting needle.

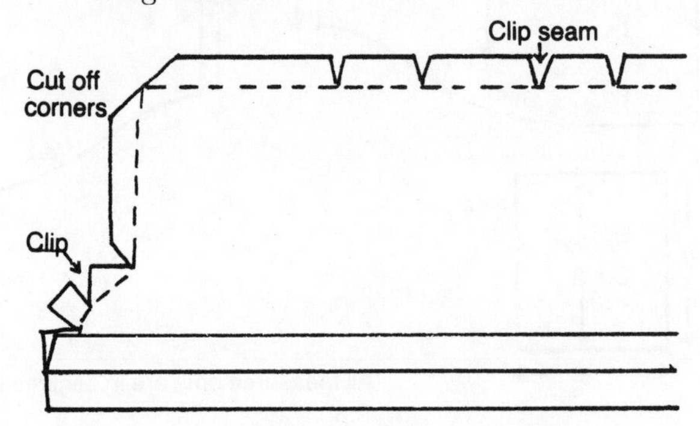

Fig. 8.22 Cutting off the corners of the collar

(10) Press front foldline back and pin on the collar as shown in Fig. 8.23.

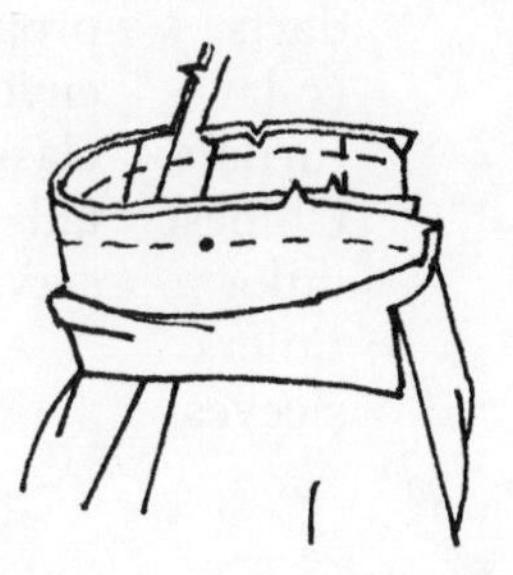

Fig. 8.23 Pinning on the collar

(11) Sew the collar onto the shirt. Clip seam and press upwards towards the collar. Hand stitch the inside of the collar to the shirt (Fig. 8.24). Press.

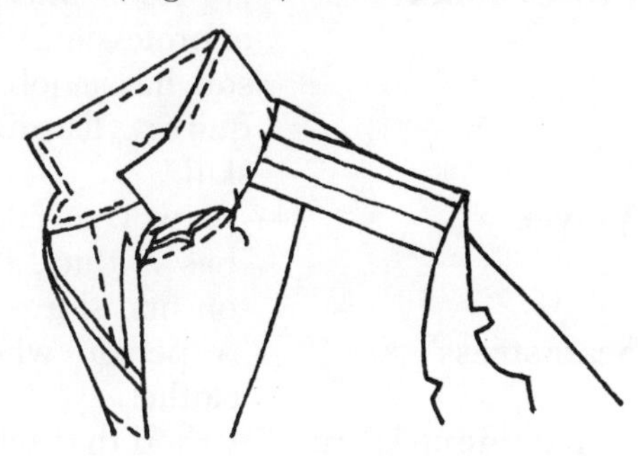

Fig. 8.24 Hand stitching the collar to the shirt

(12) Turn up the sleeve, hem 2 cm and machine stitch (Fig. 8.25). Press.

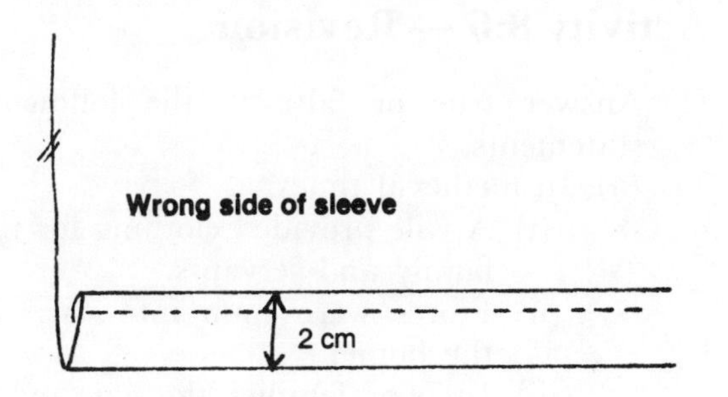

Fig. 8.25 Turning up the sleeve hem

(13) Pin and stitch the side and underarm seams all in one (Fig. 8.26). Press open and zigzag the edges.

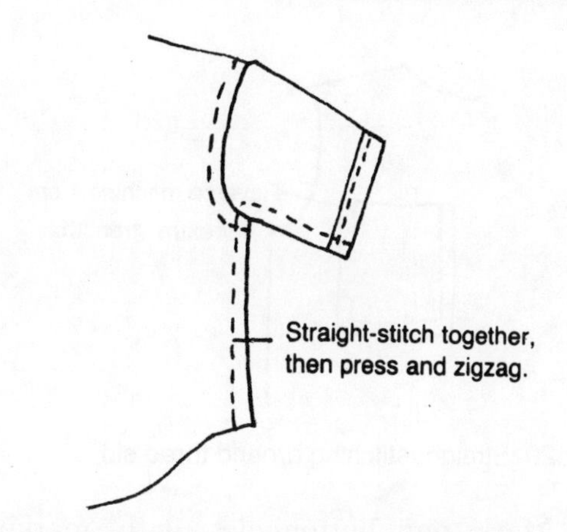

Fig. 8.26 Sewing side and underarm seams

(14) Zigzag the bottom edge of the shirt, then turn up 3 mm and press. Straight-stitch the bottom edge of the shirt (Fig. 8.27).

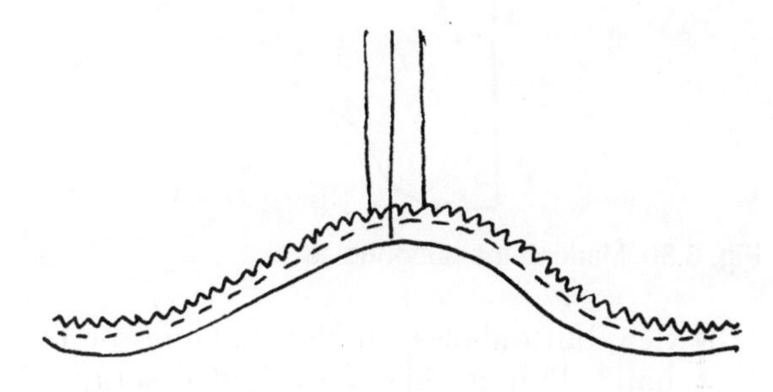

Fig. 8.27 Stitching the bottom edge of the shirt

(15) Prepare the pocket(s) for sewing (Fig. 8.28).

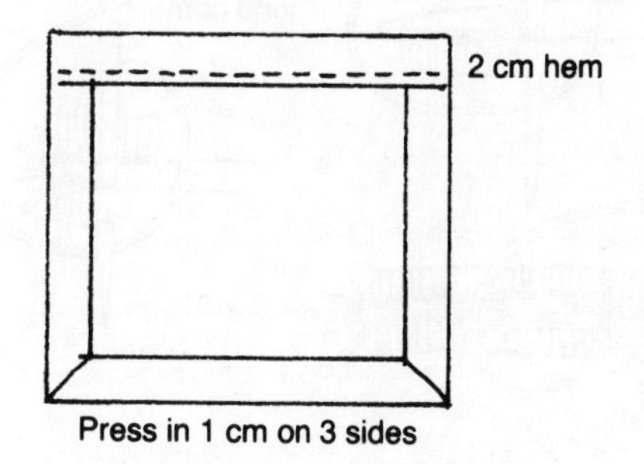

Fig. 8.28 Preparing the pocket for sewing

(16) Pin pocket(s) on the shirt and straight stitch around 3 sides (Fig. 8.29).

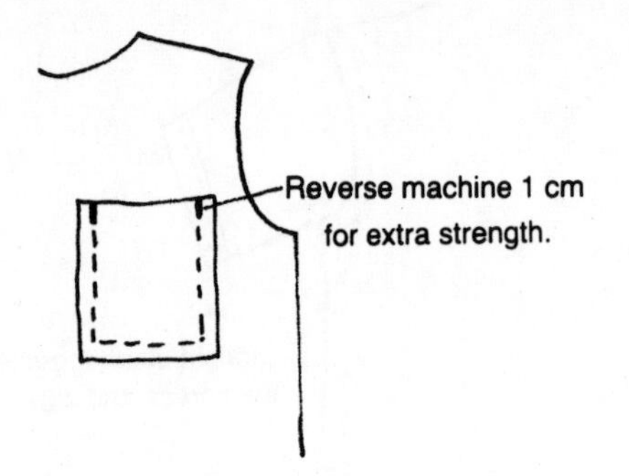

Fig. 8.29 Straight stitching around three sides

(17) Mark out buttonholes with marking chalk.

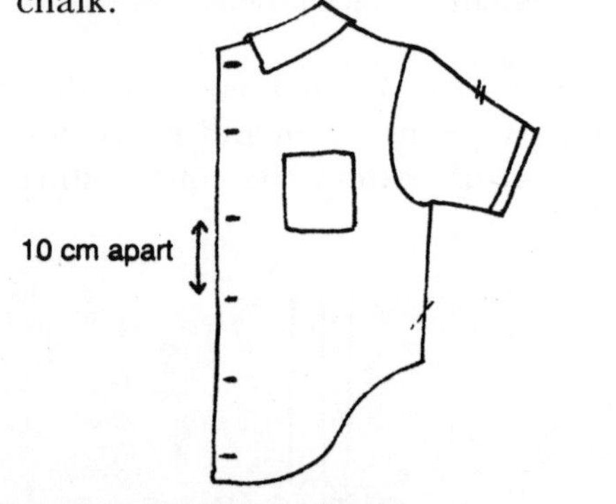

Fig. 8.30 Marking the buttonholes

(18) Sew buttonholes on the machine or by hand. Practise first on a folded scrap of fabric.

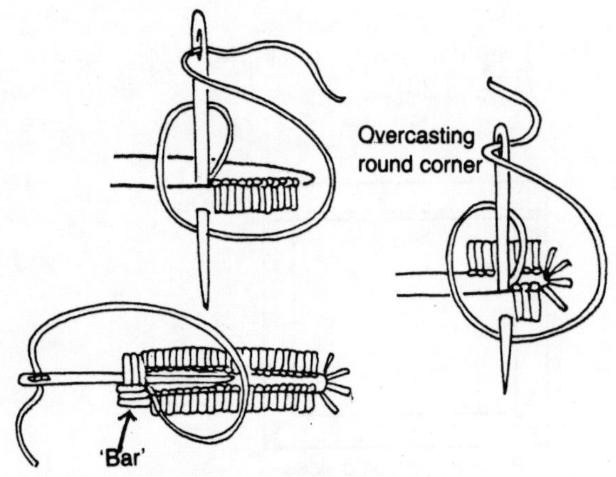

NB: Make buttonholes 2 mm larger than the diameter of your button.

Fig. 8.31 Making buttonholes by hand

(19) Press shirt well, then sew buttons on securely.

Words to remember

medieval	basic	trousers
professional	darts	proportion
velvet	collar	envelope
seamstress	turtle	classic
cravat	Chinese	fad
department	tailor	servants
Victorian	sailors	
haberdashery	sleeves	

Glossary

Medieval — Referring to the period from about 1000 to 1400. Also known as the Middle Ages in Europe and Britain.

Professional — A person who practises a profession. The person has a job that requires learning and skill.

Velvet — A woven fabric that has a thick fibre pile on one side.

Seamstress — A person who makes clothes.

Department store — A shop that sells a very large variety of items, e.g. David Jones.

Proportion — Relationship between the size of the parts.

Activity 8:6 — Revision

(1) Answer true or false to the following statements.
  (a) In medieval times:
    (i) A wife provided clothing for the family and servants.
    (ii) Fibres were spun into yarn in the home.
    (iii) In poor families the wife made the clothes herself.
  (b) A tailor made clothes for men only.
  (c) Department stores sell one range of goods.
  (d) Commercial patterns are paper patterns with instructions for a modern style.

(e) Commercial patterns are selected from a pattern book.
(f) A dart is used to shape wove: fabric to fit the body.
(g) All fashions are developed from basic patterns.
(h) Fashion fads are worn for many seasons.

(2) Match the pattern pieces with the styles in Fig. 8.32.

Fig. 8.32

9

Textiles and other cultures

People in most countries today wear clothes that are very similar. This is a result of improved communications, which make it easy for people to know what people are doing in other countries.

Many countries, however, still have a *national costume*. A national costume is the clothing style that people of a country have worn for many generations. The style has changed very little and people identify with the costume. Today, national costumes are mainly worn on special occasions such as weddings and festivals.

Activity 9:1

Select one country of your choice and find out what national costume they have. Draw pictures of their national costume.

Clothing from Eastern Europe

For many generations people changed their clothing style very little. Sometimes a style was altered by adapting aspects of dress from other people. Although villages were often close together, clothes would be slightly different in each. People had a strong sense of belonging to a village and families would live in one village for many generations. Differences of dress involved maybe a simple variation of hairstyle. For example, women in one village may have plaited the front of their hair while in another village they may have twisted it. Other differences included such things as the cut and decoration of aprons and waistcoats.

Two main influences on dress have come from the *Slavic* dress and the *Turkish* dress. Fine materials, gold threads, coins and dangling ornaments were worn. Clothing styles included wide sashes, flowing veils, shoes with turned-up toes and full trousers worn by men in many regions.

The natural fibres used to make cloth were flax and hemp from plants and wool and hair from sheep and goats. Flax was made into a heavy linen. Both flax and hemp were used for skirts, *chemises*, aprons, summer shirts and trousers. Flax is a strong fibre, and so cloth made from it lasted a long time. Woollen materials were made from sheep's wool or goat's hair and a heavy, bulky, hard-wearing cloth was constructed. The cloth was waterproof because the natural oils were left in the wool. To produce thicker cloth, the wool was *felted*. Women often carried a *distaff* with them so that they could spin during any spare moments.

Garments were cut to waste very little cloth. The cloth was too thick to sew a seam and was joined edge to edge. Embroidery was used to cover these joins. Sheepskin was used to make coats and cloaks. Decoration was either embroidery or leather appliqué.

Male and female clothing

Men generally wore coats and trousers of natural coloured felt and a white linen tunic with a woven girdle. A big woollen cloak was

Left: Slavic 'white costume', Poland
Right: Albanian city dress, with Turkish influence

Fig. 9.1 Map of Eastern Europe with national costumes from Czechoslovakia, Poland and Albania also worn. Women wore white chemises. Over the chemise they wore 'two-apron' skirts, one apron worn at the front and the other at the back.

Footwear

Footwear was simple and functional. For winter, heavy felt boots were worn. Shoes were sometimes made of interwoven strips of bark. Sandals were made from tough cowhide or pig skin. These were drawn up around the feet with leather thongs and the piece left at the toe was made into a point or blunt upturned end. Decoration was often added to footwear to create interest.

Jewellery

Peasants wore jewellery that was often handed down from generation to generation. Some jewellery was worn to ward off evil or to bring good fortune. Jewellery was worn to show wealth and *status*. In many places, young married women wore the dowry their family had paid for them. This would include coins, chains and other jewellery.

From pedlars at the markets, women would buy coloured silk, gold and silver thread, lace, cords and all kinds of ornamental ribbons and braids.

Fig. 9.2 The 'golden dress'

Mass production

As machine-produced fabrics became available, clothing changed. Printed cotton and *brocades* were used. White calico allowed people to make very full sleeves, petticoats and trousers. Machine-produced fabric draped in more graceful folds than the heavy fabric made at home. From the eighteenth and nineteenth centuries onwards, clothing became more elegant. As a result of the use of factory-produced fabric and the influence of people from other lands, folk costumes were no longer worn every day but were kept for special occasions.

Clothing from Greece

The people of Greece have known many wars and foreign occupations. Clothing was simple, but people took pride in their home-spun clothing. After the seventeenth century, silk, brocade and embroidery were included. The wearing of silver ornaments, chains and coins became frequent. The Greek Islands all have their own costumes. Some still wear them on special occasions.

The golden dress

In many parts of Greece this dress was worn by the richer peasants. The dress was so named because it was covered with heavy gold embroidery. Worn on special occasions, this was the bridal dress. The skirt, *bodice* and double jacket are embroidered in gold. The bodice is hidden by a front section which has gold beads and coins sewn on it. The young girl's hair is worn in a long plait. At the end of the plait an ornament is worn, known as a *peskoulia*.

The bridegroom's coat

The young shepherd wears a *fustanella*. It developed from the military tunic and is now rarely worn except by some regiments. The *fustanella* has two hundred pleats. It is called the 'bridegroom's coat' because, if the bride could afford to, she would send one to her groom. Under the fustanella, the bridegroom wears white trousers, dark blue or black *gaiters* and *tasselled garters* into which his name and the date of his marriage are woven. He also wears a red cap with a long black tassle and a double-breasted navy-blue waistcoat.

Fig. 9.3 Shepherd wearing a fustanella or bridegroom's coat

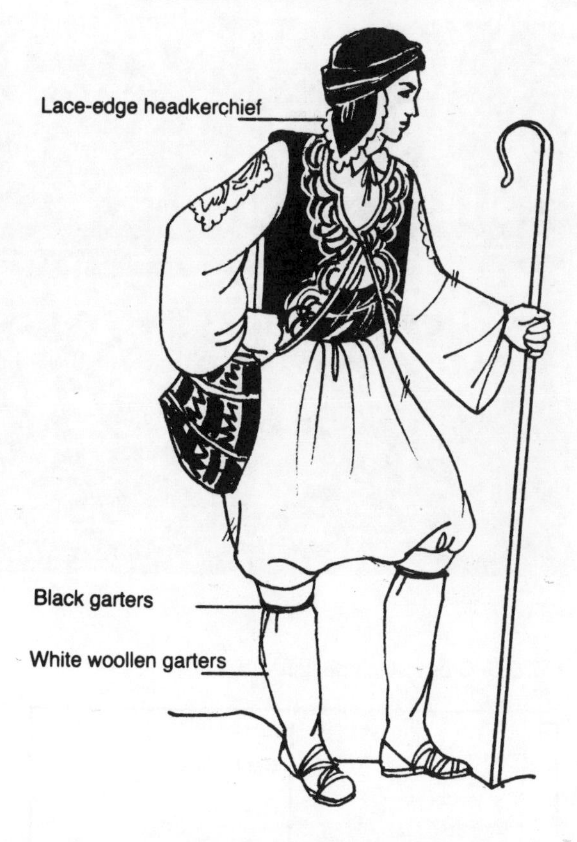

Fig. 9.4 A Greek shepherd from the island of Skyros

The shepherd wears a linen shirt that has wide embroidered sleeves. His trousers are also very wide and made out of blue cotton. A *sash* worn around the waist and an embroidered waistcoat add interest to the clothing. Sandals are worn over white woollen gaiters with black garters worn around the top. The *headkerchief* is important as it tells people the district he comes from. Two important items for a shepherd to have are a shoulder bag and a crook.

Greek embroidery

Greece is made up of many islands. These islands have developed their embroidery styles over many centuries. The main fabric used is cotton or linen. Embroidery stitches vary, but the main stitches used are chain stitch, cross stitch, herringbone stitch and satin stitch. One of the main stitches used is known as *patiti*. This stitch is like darning and is worked over five threads and under one stitch.

Counted thread work is the main form of embroidery. The work is bright with more than one colour. The main colour selected is usually red. Popular designs for embroidery include the double breasted eagle and peacock, floral motifs, the tree of life and winged animals. Narrow borders for clothing and household items are sometimes worked in repeating geometric satin stitch. Motifs may include zigzag or an eight-pointed star.

Fig. 9.5 Cross-stitch design

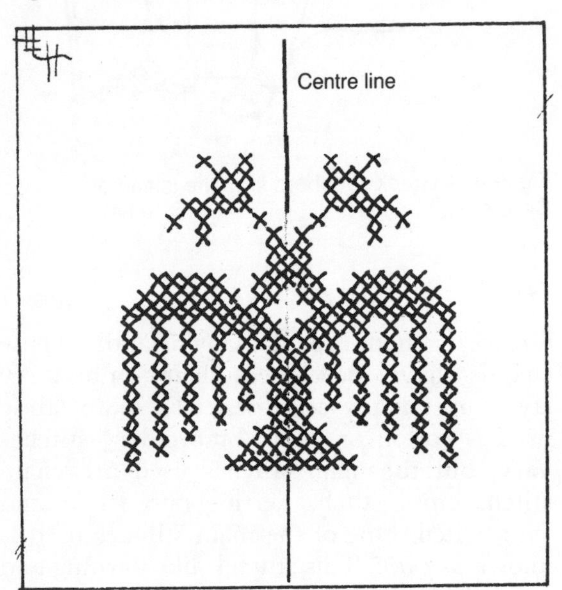

Fig. 9.6a Double-headed symmetrical bird (cross-stitch)

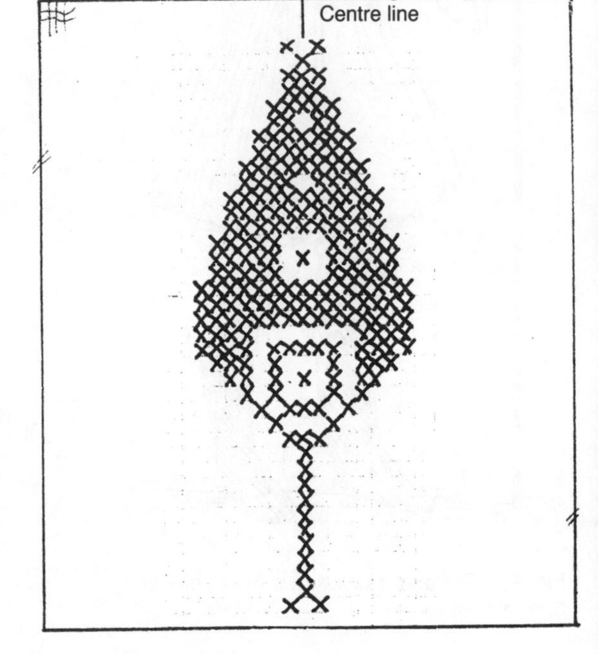

Fig. 9.6b Tree of life (green cross-stitch)

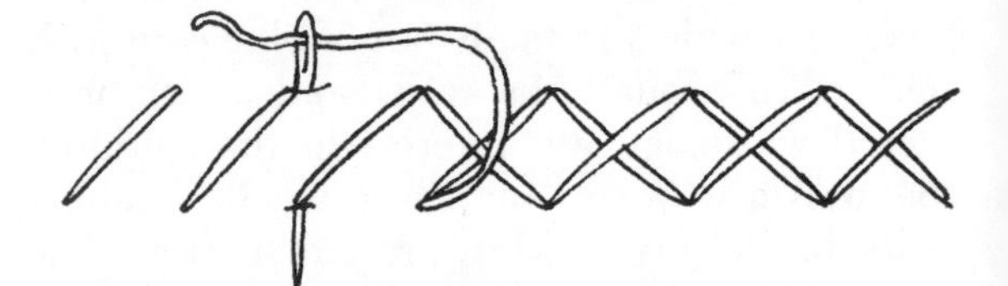

- Work in rows across the design from left to right. Keep needle straight.
- Make diagonal stitches to upper right corners *to make half the stitch*.
- *To make the second half*, work back from right to left.

Fig. 9.6c Cross-stitch

Activity 9:1 — Glasses case

You will need

- Fabric and fabric lining
- Embroidery thread
- Bias binding
- Needles
- Pins

Method

(1) Select a cross-stitch motif from Figs 9.6a and 9.6b.

(2) Cut even weave linen into 2 rectangles. *Rectangle 1* — 290 mm × 100 mm. Curve the top and bottom. *Note* the top is curved a bit more than the bottom (Fig. 9.7).
Rectangle 2 — 180 mm × 100 mm. Curve the bottom. The top is to fan out to 130 mm to allow for glasses to fit in.

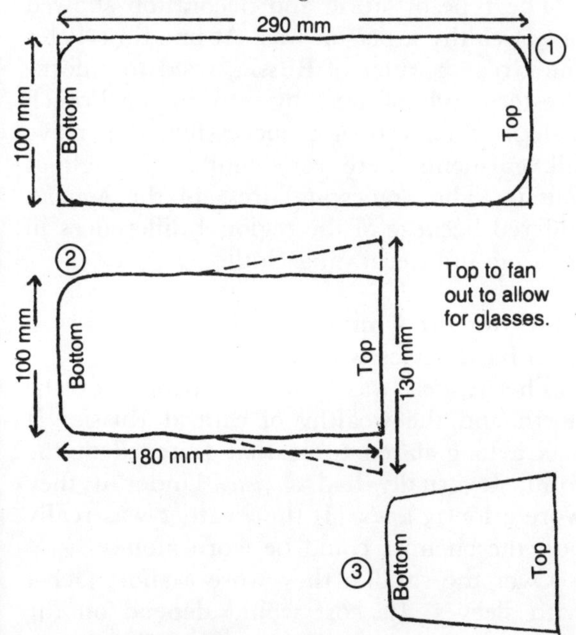

Fig. 9.7 Rectangles to be cut

(3) Cut two pieces of lining fabric the same size.

(4) The cross-stitch motif is done on the bottom half of the short fabric.

(5) Count the threads across the fabric. Find half way (Fig. 9.8). Mark with a pin then tack a straight line. This marks the centre of your work.

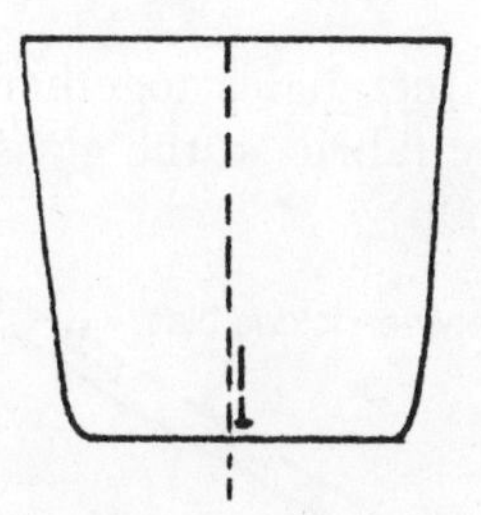

Fig. 9.8 Finding half way

(6) Zigzag around all the raw edges. Using the design selected, start your cross-stitch. Remember to keep the cross-stitch going in the one direction. When completed, press the work on the *wrong* side.

(7) *Rectangle 1* — Put the wrong sides of the fabric and lining together. Machine around the edge to hold in place.
Rectangle 2 — Put the wrong sides of the fabric and lining together. Machine around the edge to hold in place.

(8) On the shorter rectangle, turn the top under 1.5 cm and machine (Fig. 9.9a).

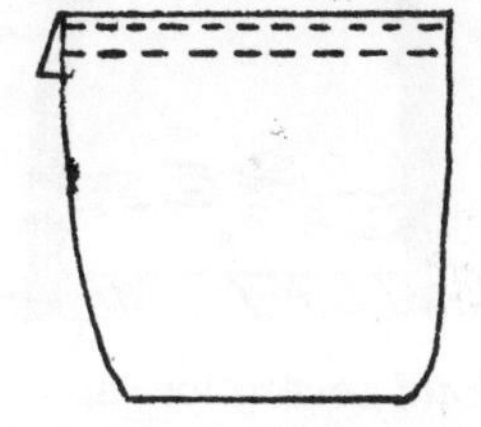

Complete 2 rows of machine stitching.

Fig. 9.9a Stitching top of glasses case

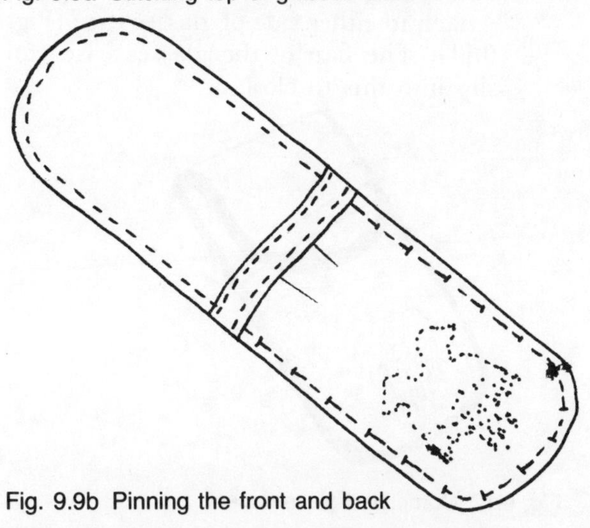

Fig. 9.9b Pinning the front and back

(9) Put the 2 rectangles together. This will leave spare fabric so the glasses can slip in (Fig. 9.9b)

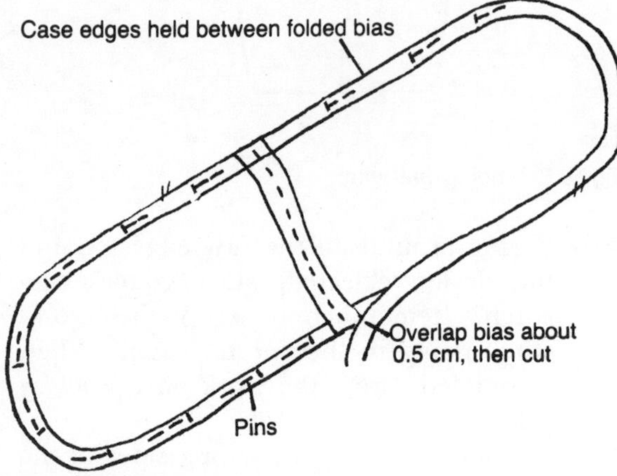

Fig. 9.10 Binding the sides

(10) Folding the bias binding in half, pin around the outside (Fig. 9.10). Machine using medium sized zigzag stitch.

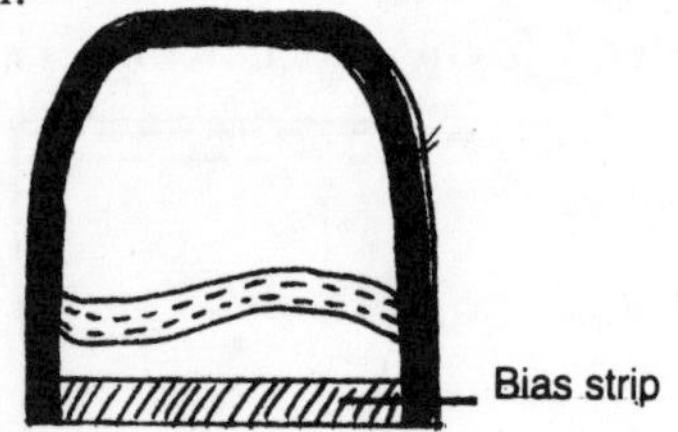

Fig. 9.11 Front section for flap

(11) Fold a piece of bias 100 mm long, in half and machine.
Attach to either side of glasses case (Fig. 9.11). The flap of the glasses case can slip into this to close.

Fig. 9.12 Completed glasses case

USSR

Russia

By the early part of this century (1917), the dress of the different regions had been replaced by a more common dress style. Now, the clothing worn by villages or regions is kept for special occasions. The heavyweight clothing worn in Russia is needed because, although summer may be hot in some regions, many regions experience extreme cold and people need protection.

In Russia the main variations were in the clothing of women. Men's clothing was plainer and more uniform in style. Decoration was used a lot on clothes, especially shirts and summer *breeches*. The shirts had a common style with a high collar and opening on one side.

The type of fabric and decoration showed how wealthy a person was. At one time Peter the Great, a ruler of Russia, tried to enforce Western style of dress by introducing French fashion, but was not successful. Expensive silk garments were very similar throughout Russia. The homespun dress of the *peasants* differed because of the regional differences in making and decorating cloth.

Clothing for women

Two basic styles were worn.

The *sarafan* was worn by people of the north and the wealthy of central Russia. It was a long flared tunic that fastened at the front. It usually had a *yoke*. Under it they wore a long *chemise*. If the weather was really hot, the chemise could be worn alone.

Over the sarafan they wore a short jacket with sleeves. Its cost would depend on the richness of the decoration. Their headdress was interesting and varied. Often it was expensive, being made of rich fabrics and embroidered and ornamented with glass or jewels, especially pearls. Headdresses were valuable heirlooms and were most often used for weddings.

In the south and part of the centre of Russia, people wore the *poneva* although a silk sarafan could also be worn. The poneva was a skirt worn over a chemise, usually with a long apron or a pinafore. A loose, straight-sleeved tunic was also worn with a shawl and open coat when necessary. Clothes were still patterned. In winter, felt boots rather than leather were worn for warmth. In the south, headdresses were complicated and had many parts, pom-poms, points, horns and hanging ribbons as decoration. Although not made of precious materials, they were rich in work and bright in colour.

Styles became simpler and garments became less elaborate as bought cloth was used more and more. Headdresses too became plainer with women now wearing a head-shawl or scarf.

Fig. 9.13 Greater Russia. Typical peasant dress of the nineteenth century

Fig. 9.14 Nineteenth century South Russian woman

As we have mentioned earlier, Russia is made up of many regions. The regions to be examined more closely include:

- The Ukraine.
- Lithuania.
- Ryazan and Tula districts.
- Archangel, the northern part of Russia.

The Ukraine

Styles were simple in the Ukraine with a basic garment (*plakhta*) worn over the chemise. A checked or tartan skirt with an apron covering the front gap was worn. A popular form of dress was the three-quarter length, fitted sleeveless jacket, fastening to one side of the front. The headdress was a cap and veil which was eventually changed to a manufactured head scarf. Aprons began to be purchased. These were made of printed calico. The Ukraine is known for its beautiful embroidered blouses featuring floral patterns. Red boots were the favourite footwear.

Fig. 9.15 People in dancing festival costume

Fig. 9.16 Girls doing a hat dance

Lithuania

Clothing was similar to other *Baltic* states.

Men — The main clothing worn was homespun and included shirts, trousers, waistcoats and coats with variations in the colours and weaving patterns used.

Women — Chemises, skirts, bodices, aprons and for the most part, *circlet* headdresses with veils and streamers at the back were worn. The main variations were in the cut of the bodices and the patterns on the aprons and chemises. The shape and decoration of the headdresses also varied.

Tradition is observed in the clothing worn by older people. In this case, the old woman is wearing a dark blue coat called 'the coat of a hundred pleats' and a white *wimple* headdress.

Fig. 9.17 Old peasant woman

Ryazan and Tula districts in Greater Russia

Men — Men wore dark, heavy, woollen coats, woven girdles, and fur caps with flaps to keep ears warm.

Women — south of Moscow, women wore homespun skirts and straight tunics, often with long waistcoats. The girls wore skirts or *sarafans*. Those worn by the girls were black and those worn by the brides were red. Bright colours, mainly red, were used in the varied patterns on the clothes. In summer, peasants often went barefooted. Leather shoes and boots and shoes made of interwoven strips of bark were also worn. During times of extreme cold, high boots of thick felt provided the most effective insulation.

Fig. 9.18 Man wearing winter clothes

Fig. 9.19 Festival dress from the Tula and Ryazan districts

Archangel — northern part of Greater Russia

The richness of the clothes worn by these people was due to the trading they did. Gold, furs, jewels and river pearls provided their stock.

Men — *Tunics*, fastened at the side. *Girdles* were narrow. Trousers were made of patterned woven material. Because the weather is very cold for most of the year, felt boots, fur coats and caps are still worn today. To add extra warmth, the fur is worn on the inside where it traps a layer of warm air and makes the clothes warmer to wear.

Women — Women wore the sarafan with undersleeves. The sleeves were often embroidered. The headdress looked like a halo and was often ornamented with silver, pearls and jewels.

The richly decorated dress included red cuffs decorated with pearls and buttons surrounded with gold lace worn with many expensive necklaces.

Fig. 9.20 Woman wearing a sarafan

Embroidery

Russia is rich in embroidery materials. The textile resources include flax, wool and cotton. Leather and, in certain areas, reindeer skins are embroidered. Reindeer hair is used for embroidery threads. Red is the most popular colour and is generally used on a natural colour linen. The most popular embroidery stitch is the cross stitch. Other popular stitches include: back stitch, buttonhole stitch, chain stitch, satin stitch and pattern darning. Depending on the region, embroidery designs include eagles and other birds as well as narrow borders of repeating geometric motifs.

Embroidery in the Ukraine

Embroidery is still very popular in the Ukraine where silk and cotton threads are used. Popular colours are bright shades of maroon, red, orange, green, gold and violet. Pastel shades are seldom seen. The most popular embroidery stitches include back stitch, buttonhole stitch, needle chain stitch, cross stitch, satin stitch, stem stitch, needle weaving, pattern darning and drawn thread work.

Pattern darning

This is worked using close parallel lines of long vertical darning stitch. The colours used are generally black or maroon. Embroidered on the wrong side, the fabric will later be turned over and the gaps in the design filled with straight stitches.

Fig. 9.21 Pattern darning

Fig. 9.22 Adaptation of darning

Activity 9:2 — Pattern darned place mats

You will need

- Even weave fabric (similar to hessian)
- Stranded embroidery thread in 2 colours
- Needles and scissors

Method

(1) To prepare one place mat, cut fabric 32 cm × 45 cm.
(2) Zigzag, using small stitches, 2 cm in from the raw edge all the way around.
(3) Position your darning needle to the left of the place mat.
(4) Using the main colour you have selected, begin darning.
(5) When you have completed the first colour, start the second colour.
(6) Fringe the edges to the zigzag stitching.
(7) Press on the wrong side.
(8) Repeat the above if you would like to make a set.

Further reading

Fanning, R. & T., *Here and Now Stitchery from Other Times and Places*, Butterick Publishing, New York, 1978

Fox, L.M., *Folk Costumes from Eastern Europe*, Chatto and Windus, London, 1977

Gostelow, M., *Embroidery, Traditional Designs, Techniques and Patterns from all over the World*, Marshall Cavendish, London, 1982

Snowden, J., *The Folk Dress of Europe*, Mayflower Books, New York, 1979

Words to remember

national	peskoulia	poneva
costume	fustanella	circlet
Slavic	military	wimple
chemise	tunic	dowry
felted	regiment	Turkish
distaff	girdle	sarafan
peasants	crook	pedlars
gaiters	breeches	garters
brocades	homespun	appliqué
bodice	yoke	status

Glossary

Chemise — Undergarment, usually long.
Felted — Heavy cloth made by matting wool fibres together.
Distaff — Cleft stick. Wool or flax was wound on to it when people spun fibres into yarn by hand.
Peasants — People who worked the land; poor.
Pedlars — Person who travels around selling goods.
Brocade — Very richly decorated fabric made from expensive yarn.
Bodice — Close-fitting upper part of female dress.
Dowry — Goods a woman takes to her marriage.
Wimple — Head covering of fabric arranged in folds.
Sarafan — Woman's dress.
Yoke — Separately made shoulder piece of shirt or dress.
Poneva — Skirt worn in Russia.
Girdle — Belt worn around the waist.

Activity 9:3 — Revision

The following questions are to be answered in your workbook after reading the text.

(1) Explain the meaning of the term 'national costume'.
(2) How could a traveller tell which village a person came from in Eastern Europe?
(3) List the natural fibres that have been used to make clothing.
(4) What do the natural oils of wool do to a garment?
(5) Why were clothes sewn with pattern pieces edge to edge?
(6) Indicate why you think embroidery on clothing was so popular.
(7) How did mass production of fabric effect the style of clothing?
(8) What is a golden dress?
(9) Explain the design of the fustanella.
(10) What is one of the most important embroidery stitches in Greece?
(11) List 3 other embroidery stitches used in Greece.
(12) Describe a sarafan.

(13) How did the clothing of the north and south of the USSR differ?
(14) Which two colours are frequently used for embroidery in the Ukraine?
(15) Describe the technique of pattern darning.

Activity 9:4 — Wonderword

(1) Find the following words in the wonderword.

national
costume
villages
chemise
apron
wool
flax
felt
distaff
embroidery
appliqué
girdle
peasants
jewellery
status
dowry
gaiters
garter
crook
satin
cross
patiti
herringbone
eagle
motif
animal
sarafan
region
yoke
poneva
Russia
tradition
man
woman
wimple
tunic
cloak

N	A	T	I	O	N	A	L	C	O	S	T	U	M	E	M
A	P	C	S	A	S	P	S	H	P	R	O	D	A	M	U
C	R	R	F	V	A	P	R	E	G	I	O	N	N	B	C
W	O	O	L	E	R	L	T	M	I	O	N	H	Y	R	A
O	N	O	A	N	A	I	G	I	R	D	L	E	O	O	S
M	S	K	X	O	F	O	M	S	E	I	D	S	K	I	A
E	A	N	T	P	A	U	R	E	E	S	S	O	E	D	F
N	T	G	I	E	N	E	O	N	C	T	A	L	W	E	K
V	I	L	L	A	G	E	S	I	L	A	O	T	L	R	H
M	N	C	W	S	A	A	N	T	I	F	N	T	N	Y	Y
O	G	L	I	A	R	U	I	S	A	F	T	I	Y	L	E
T	S	O	M	N	T	P	A	T	I	T	I	A	N	R	E
I	W	A	P	T	E	A	G	L	E	O	U	R	N	A	O
F	N	K	L	S	R	L	Y	A	T	R	F	S	E	S	L
J	E	W	E	L	L	E	R	Y	R	U	S	S	I	A	T
H	E	R	R	I	N	G	B	O	N	E	I	V	A	L	S

Note: Some words are written backwards.

(2) Using the left-over letters, fill in the blanks to make a sentence about clothing.

_ _ _ _   _ _ _ _ _ _ _ _ _ _

_ _ _   _ _ _ _ _   _ _ _ _ _ _ _ _

_ _ _ _ _ _ _ _   _ _ _ _ _ _   _ _ _

_ _ _ _   _ _ _ _   _ _

_ _ _ _ _ _ _ _ _.

10

Textiles for fun

Many of the activities in this chapter can be made very quickly using simple materials. You may have to refer back to earlier chapters to remind you of some skills necessary to complete the article.
Make sure that you complete the questions in your workbook after completing each activity. And most importantly, have ***fun***!

Activity 10:1 — Christmas tree decorations

Fig. 10.1 Christmas decorations

You will need

- Scraps of felt
- 1.5 mm wide satin ribbon in red, green or gold for each decoration
- Nylon wadding or cotton filling
- Braid and ribbon scraps

Method

(1) Cut out 2 pieces of felt for each bauble using the guides in Fig. 10.2, or make up your own designs.

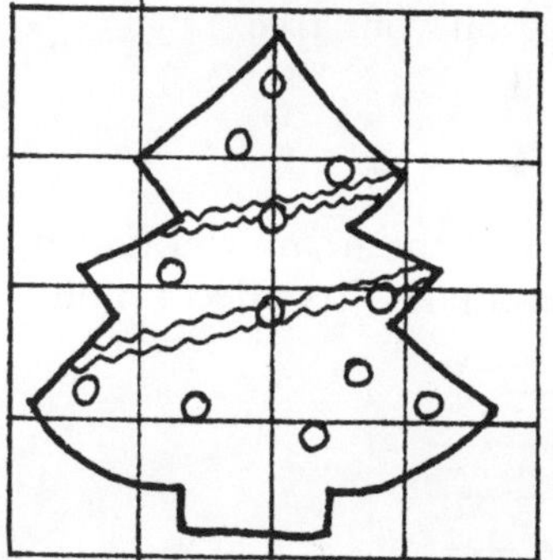

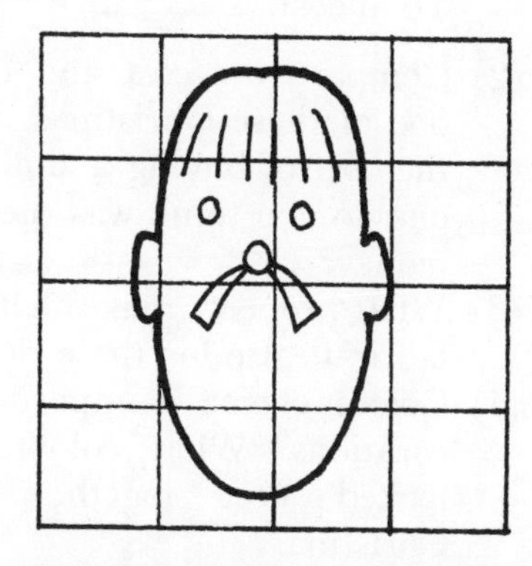

Fig. 10.2 Graphs of designs for candy cane, Santa, and Christmas tree decorations

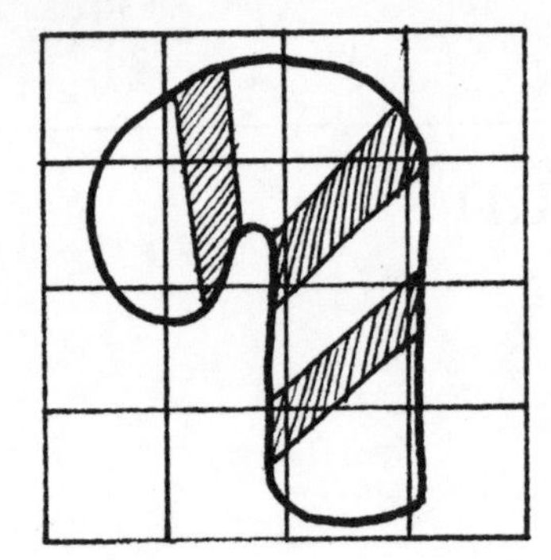

(2) Using a tapestry needle and a 50 cm length of ribbon, oversew the edges, or machine stitch around the outside. Leave a small opening to stuff the decoration with filling.
(3) After you have filled the bauble with some wadding, embroider with simple stitches and different coloured ribbon for decoration and character. Use ribbon to tie over-hand knots for eyes and Christmas tree lights; thick ribbon on the candy cane, and strips of braid for baubles.
(4) Loop ribbon through the top and tie securely to hang on your tree.

10:1 — Revision

(1) Add up the cost of the items you had to buy especially to make these decorations.

- Felt: ________
- Ribbon: ________
- Braid: ________
- Filling: ________

Total cost: ________

(2) Compare the cost and effort of making one of these Christmas decorations, and the cost of buying a similar item. Which one do you think was the better value for money?
(3) What property makes felt the best type of fabric to use for these decorations?
(4) Colour choice is important for these decorations. What colours did you find looked best together, especially for Christmas?
(5) What could you use as a substitute for nylon wadding to fill the decorations?

10:1 — Extension

(1) Find out how felt is made.
(2) How can the use of contrasting and complementary colours make Christmas decorations look good?

Activity 10:2 — Sports bag

Fig. 10.3 Sports bag

You will need

- 1 m of 90 cm wide cotton fabric such as denim, drill, calico, or sailcloth
- 1 m of Velcro
- 4.6 m of 2 cm wide stripe braid or ribbon
- 2 m of 9 mm grosgrain ribbon
- Piece of thick plastic 7 cm × 10 cm
- Sewing thread to match the braid

Method

(1) Iron fabric well. Turn under a 1 cm hem on the cut edges (Fig. 10.4), as you did for the apron in Chapter 2.

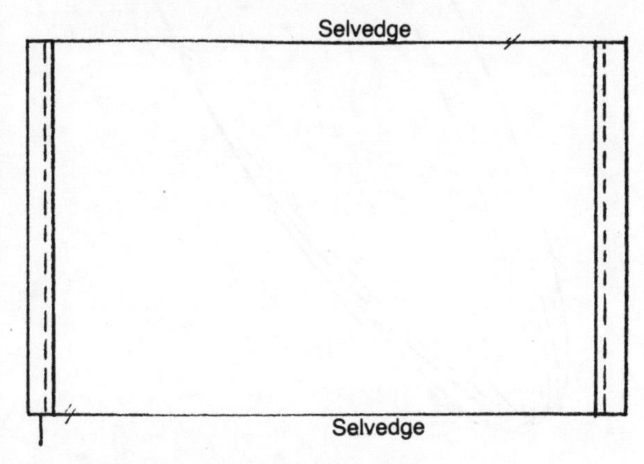

Fig. 10.4 Hems

(2) On the right side, sew 2 strips of braid using a single row of stitching, across the selvedges. Place plastic in the centre of the fabric, 12 cm from one of the selvedges.

(3) Then using the 9 mm ribbon, pin an outline for the label holder around the plastic (Fig. 10.5).

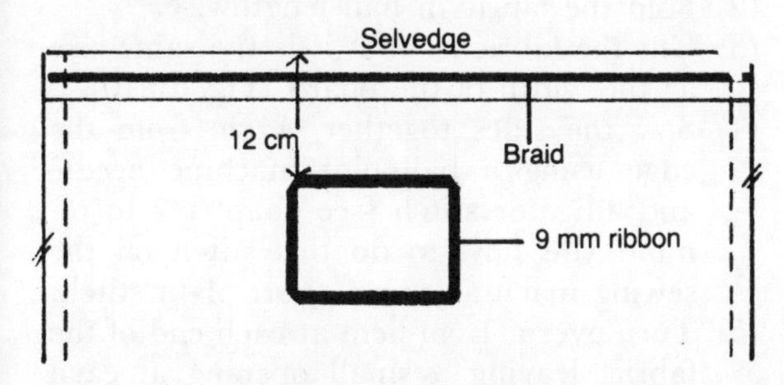

Fig. 10.5 Braid and ribbon placement

(4) Sew Velcro on to the wrong side of the fabric, under the braid.

(5) Using all the left-over braid, pin it on to the fabric as shown in the following diagram. Sew either side of the handles (Fig. 10.6) using a strong crossways stitching at the ends like you did for the apron straps in chapter 2.

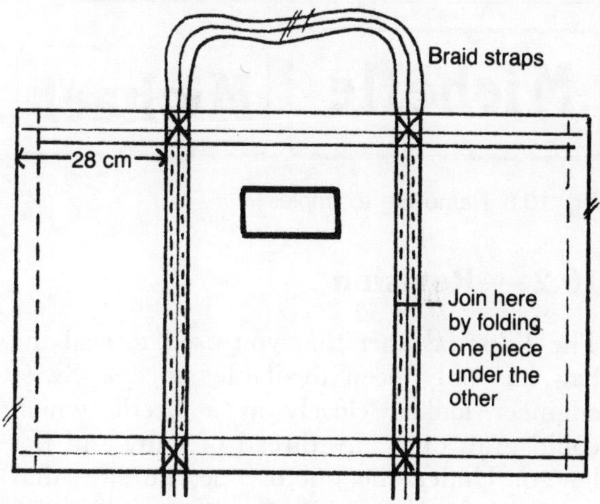

Fig. 10.6 Sewing on the braid handles

(6) Cut the left-over ribbon in half. Thread each through the guides at each end of the bag using a safety pin attached to the ribbon (Fig. 10.7). Pull up tight and tie in a knot or bow.

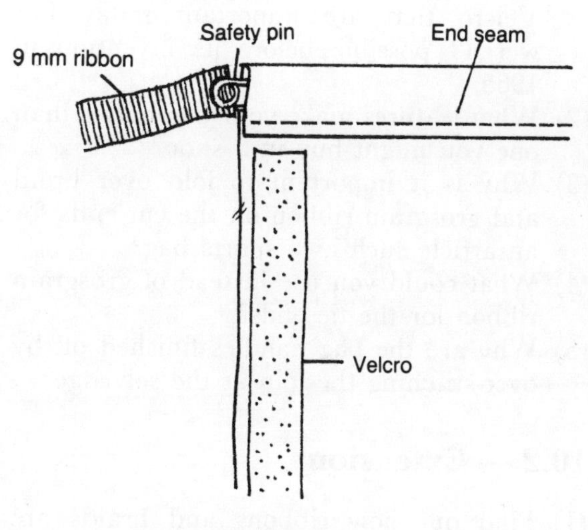

Fig. 10.7 Guiding the ribbon

(7) Make a name tag for your bag (Fig. 10.8).

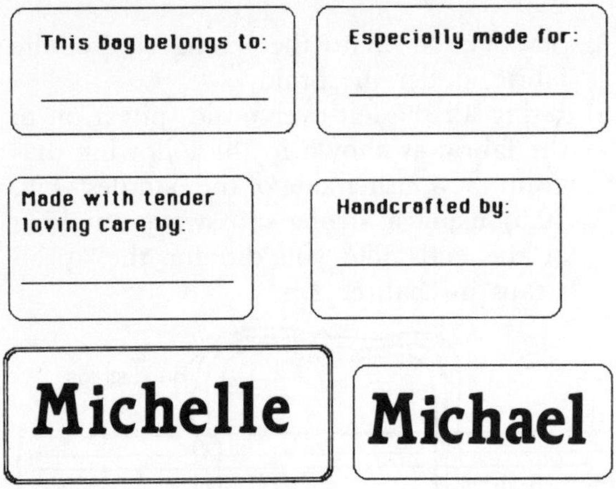

This bag belongs to:

Especially made for:

Made with tender loving care by:

Handcrafted by:

Michelle

Michael

Fig. 10.8 Name tag examples

10.2 — Revision

The *Velcro* fastener that you used to seal the bag has only been available since a Swiss engineer looked closely at a beetle which could grab onto any thread of hair, and not let go. Under the microscope, he saw that the beetle had strong hooks. After eight years and many experiments, the *Velcro* fastener was devised by using two mating nylon tapes.

(1) Look closely at the tape. You should see that one side is covered with little hooks and the other side is covered with tiny, soft loops. Make a list of the uses for Velcro that are important today but weren't possible before its invention in 1965.
(2) What features make your bag better than one you might buy in a shop?
(3) Why is it important to fold over braid and grosgrain ribbon on the cut ends for an article such as a sports bag?
(4) What could you use instead of grosgrain ribbon for the tie ends?
(5) Why are the bag handles finished off by over-stitching the join at the selvedge?

10.2 — Extension

(1) Find out how ribbons and braids are made.
(2) Look at both sides of the Velcro under the microscope. Sketch them in your workbook. Why do they seal so well?

Activity 10:3 — Surfboard cover

Fig. 10.9 Surfboard cover

You will need

- 2 m of two-way stretch terry towelling [or the length of the board plus 10 cm]
- Polyester thread to match
- 1.3 m of 6 mm wide elastic

Method

(1) Measure the width of the board at its widest point.
(2) Fold the fabric in half lengthwise.
(3) Cut the fabric so that it is the same size as the width of the board (Fig. 10.10).
(4) Sew the sides together, 1 cm from the edge using a ballpoint machine needle and alligator stitch [see chapter 2 to remind you how to do this stitch on the sewing machine], or a short plain stitch.
(5) Turn over a 1 cm hem at each end of the fabric, leaving a small opening at each end, 1 cm wide (Fig. 10.11).

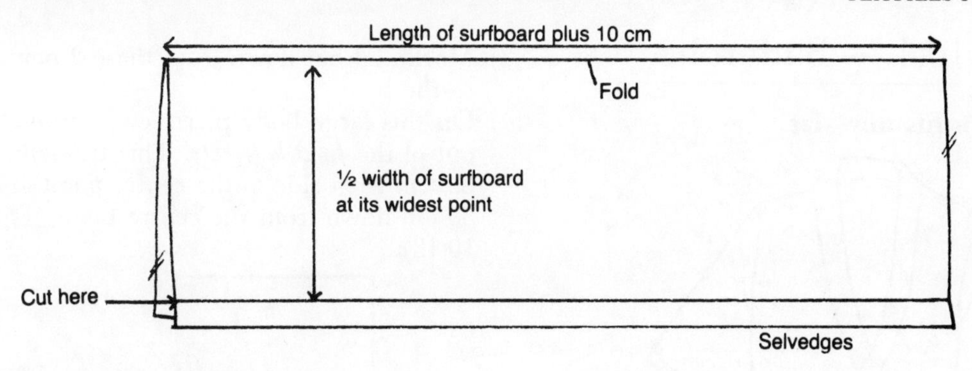

Fig. 10.10 Cover layout

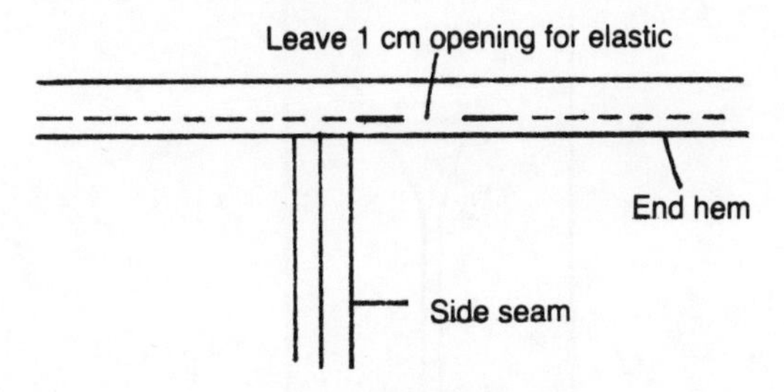

Fig. 10.11 End of cover showing elastic guide

(6) Thread elastic through one end with a small safety pin and pull tight, so that all the fabric is gathered up. Secure the elastic ends together by hand sewing.

(7) Thread the left-over elastic through the top end. This will be the end you get the board out of, so make sure you don't pull it too tight. Sew the elastic ends together.

10:3 — Revision

It is important that you use *two-way stretch fabric* for this surfboard cover, so that the cover clings to the board to prevent it flapping on the top of the car and to protect it from knocks.

(1) What is one-way stretch fabric?

(2) What uses can you list for one-way stretch fabrics?

(3) What uses can you list for two-way stretch fabrics?

(4) Why was polyester thread used instead of cotton thread for sewing the cover?

(5) What could you use instead of elastic for the opening end of the cover?

(6) What property of stretch terry towelling stops it from creasing?

10:3 — Extension

(1) Find out how stretch terry towelling is made.

(2) Test the stretchability of your terry towelling and compare it to other fabrics by stretching it horizontally along a ruler. Make sure that all your fabric samples are the same size. Fill in the following chart in your workbook: Which has the greatest percentage stretch?

Fabric name	**Stretch length**	**Percentage stretch** $\frac{\textit{original length} \times 100}{\textit{stretch length}}$

Activity 10:4 — Bath robe

This pattern fits any size!

Fig. 10.12 Bath robe

You will need

- 2 m of 90 cm wide fabric such as woven terry towelling, stretch terry towelling, or velour.
- Thread to match
- 4 m of 4 cm wide cotton braid

Method

(1) Fold the fabric in half and find the centre.

(2) Measurement A is your measurement from shoulder to shoulder.

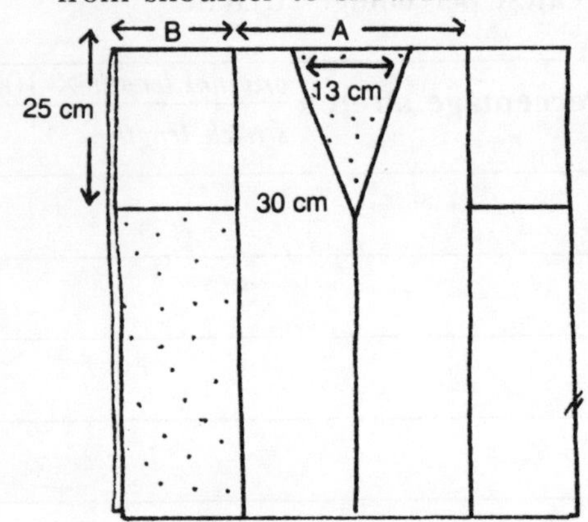

Fig. 10.13 Cutting layout

(3) Mark and cut down from these 2 points to the hem.

(4) On this large body piece, cut a triangle out of the *front half only*. This triangle is 6.5 cm each side of the centre point and 30 cm down from the centre point (Fig. 10.13).

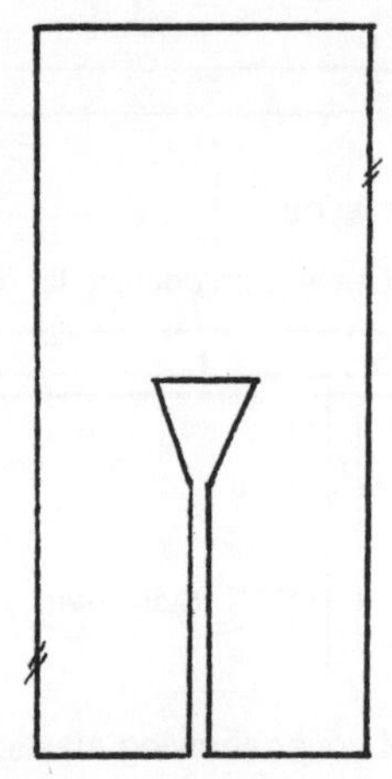

Fig. 10.14 Front cutting guide

(5) Cut up the centre line to the triangle on the *front only* (Fig. 10.14).

(6) Measurement B is the length you want the sleeve from the shoulder edge.

(7) Turn over and hem 1 cm from the bottom of the sleeves.

(8) Lay the sleeves flat on the body part on the right side, then stitch together (Fig. 10.15).

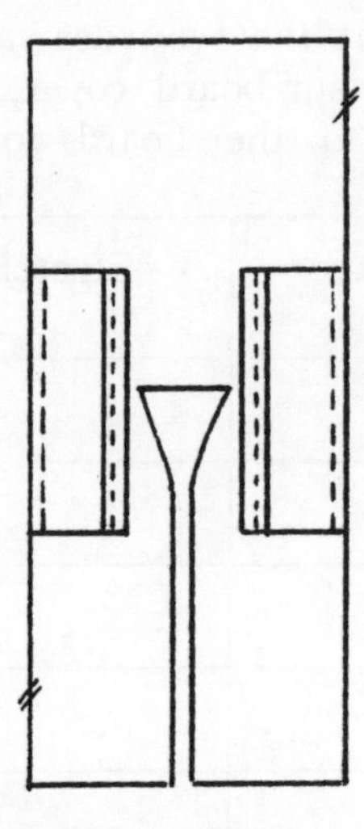

Fig. 10.15 Sewing in the sleeves

(9) On the wrong side, stitch side seams and underarm seams all in one (Fig. 10.16). Press seams open and finish them off with the best seam finish for the type of fabric used (see chapter 2: Seam finishes).

Fig. 10.16 Sewing seams and edges

(10) Hem the lower edge by hand or machine.
(11) Fold braid in half and sew it on from the front, all around the opening. Use the spare braid for the tie belt.
(12) Make patch pockets from the spare fabric (Fig. 10.17).

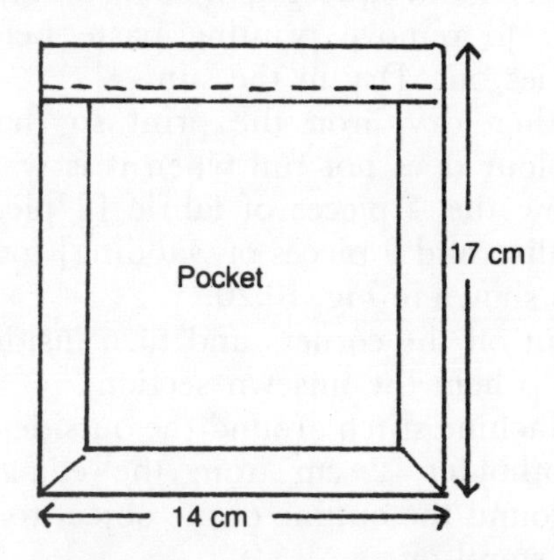

Fig. 10.17 Making the pockets

10:4 — Revision

(1) Which seam finish did you decide to use on the side and underarm seams and why?
(2) Look up the word *absorb* in a dictionary. Write down its meaning.
Bath robes are meant to be loose and comfortable. The fibres used to make the fabric also have a great influence on comfort as well as the looseness of the robe. Some fabrics are uncomfortable to wear because they do not absorb moisture. Fibres such as cotton absorb moisture well, therefore fabrics made from cotton are an excellent choice for a bathrobe.
(3) List the names of some fabrics that you think would not be suitable for a bathrobe.
(4) Why is cotton terry towelling more absorbent than say, cotton calico?

10:4 — Extension

Do an *absorbency test* on some fabric scraps. Gently place pieces of fabric cut to the same size in a sink filled with 2 cm of water. Time how long it takes for each one to sink under the surface. Then fill in the following chart in your workbook:

Fabric name	Time taken to absorb water

(1) Which fabric was the most absorbent?
(2) Which fabric was the least absorbent?
(3) Write a list of all the factors that could affect fabric absorbency.

Activity 10:5 — Screenprinted potholder

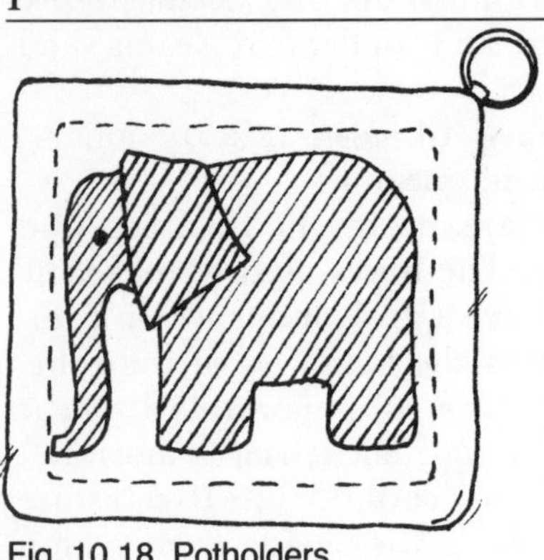

Fig. 10.18 Potholders

You will need

- 2 × 20 cm square pieces of light coloured fabric such as unbleached calico
- 2 pieces of nylon wadding 20 cm square
- Thread to match
- Thick drawing paper and newspaper
- Sharp scissors or Stanley knife
- A piece of wood 30 × 30 cm to rest your paper on while cutting out
- Screen printing paste and metal spoon
- Squeegee and screen

Method

(1) Decide on a design for your potholder, or use one of the designs above. A large solid object is best. Children's colouring books have some good ideas for designs.

(2) Draw the design on your paper using sharp lines.

(3) Cut out the areas of the design that are to be printed with sharp scissors or a Stanley knife.

(4) Cover your table with plenty of newspaper.

(5) Place the paper with the cut-out design on the fabric.

(6) Place the screen on top of the design, ensuring that the paper overhangs on all four sides of the screen.

(7) Place 2 tablespoons of printing paste on top of the screen.

(8) Have someone hold the screen still while you squeegee the printing paste down to the part of the screen nearest to you.

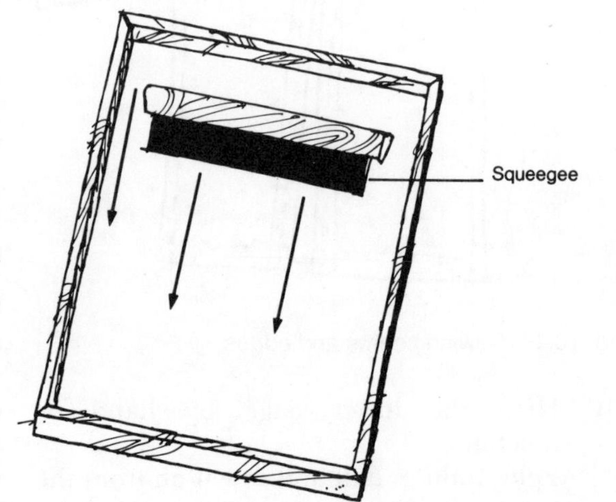

Fig. 10.19 Squeegee and screen

(9) Lift the screen off gently. Wash the screen and squeegee in cold running water to remove printing paste before it dries out. Dry in the sun.

(10) When dry, iron the print so that the colour does not run when it is washed.

(11) Sew the 4 pieces of fabric [2 pieces of calico and 2 pieces of wadding] together as shown in Fig. 10.20.

(12) Cut off the corners and turn inside out. Slip hem the unsewn section.

(13) Machine stitch around the outside of the potholder, 2 cm from the edge. Sew around the outline of the object to make it stand out.

(14) Add to the character of the design with embroidery or fabric painting pencils.

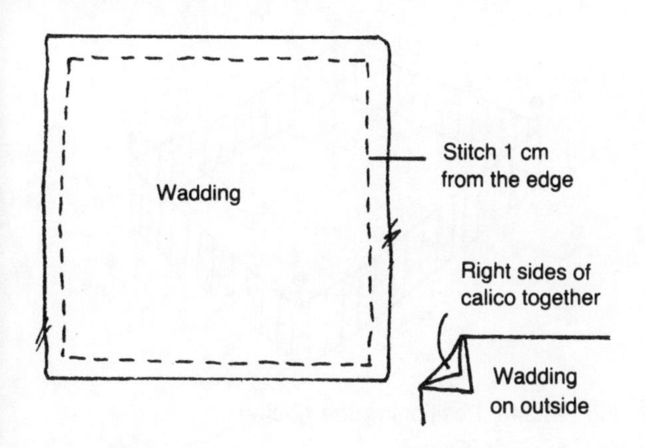

Fig. 10.20 Sewing the potholder pieces together

(15) Attach a curtain ring to one corner by hand sewing.

10:5 — Revision

(1) What makes nylon wadding a suitable filling for the potholder?
(2) What does the word *insulation* mean? [Check the Glossary in chapter 6].
(3) Make a list of other types of insulators that you know.
(4) Why is it important not to iron the potholder *after* it is completed?
(5) Why does ironing the screenprint when it is dry, stop the colour from running when washed?
(6) Find out how nylon wadding is made.

10:5 — Extension

Experiment: Fabrics as insulators
Aim: To find out which fabrics keep us warm by acting as insulators

You will need

- Metal tins with lids [all the same size]
- A thermometer for each tin
- A watch
- Pins and scissors
- Fabrics to test

Method

(1) Cut a piece of fabric to fit around the tin and pin it to make a jacket.
(2) Put a thermometer in the tin.
(3) Put hot water in every tin. Allow the water to cool until the thermometer is 50°C. Remove it and put the lid on the tin.
(4) Wait for ten minutes and take the temperature of the water.
(5) The tin with the highest temperature has the warmest jacket on.
(6) Fill in the following chart in your workbook:

Fabric name	Final temperature °C

Activity 10:6 — Beach top

This top will fit a 12 or 13 year old boy or girl.

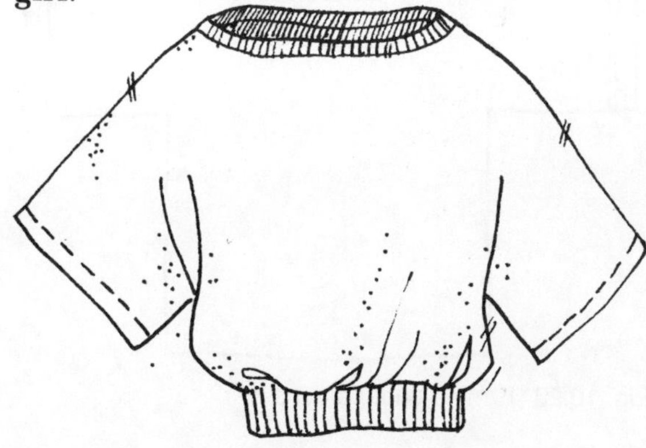

Fig. 10.21 Completed beach top

You will need

- 1 m of knit fabric such as fleecy backed cotton/polyester
- Thread to match
- A strip of 14 cm wide rib knit for the waistband

Method

(1) Fold fabric in half lengthwise.
(2) Cut out according to the pattern in Fig.

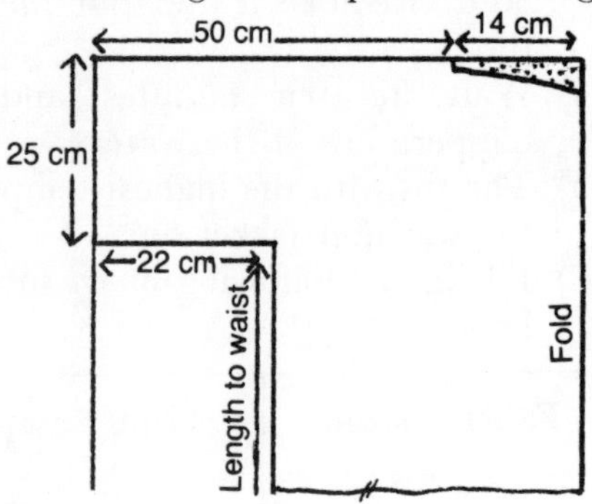

Fig. 10.22 Cutting layout

(3) Turn under a 1 cm hem on the sleeves and around the neck (Fig. 10.23).

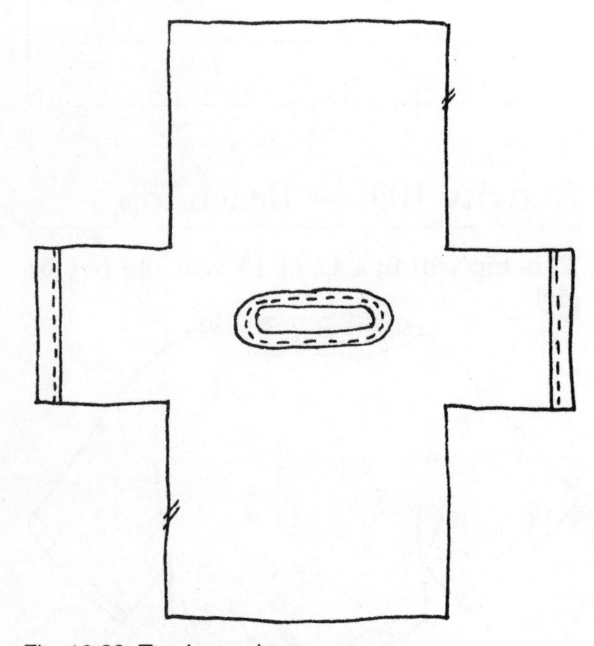

Fig. 10.23 Turning under seams

(4) Sew side and underarm seams 1 cm from the edges.
(5) Cut the rib knit so you have a piece which fits around your waist firmly. Sew the ends together with a 1 cm seam.
(6) Fold the band in half lengthwise and press flat.
(7) Pin the rib band to the top using Fig. 10.24a.

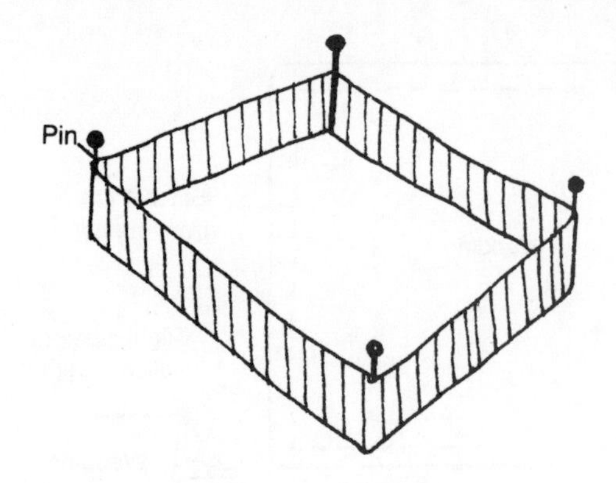

Fig. 10.24a Positioning the ribbing

- Stretch rib band to fit the waist using pins.
- The band and top are divided into 4 equal quarters.

Fig. 10.24b Attaching the rib band

(8) Attach the double waist band to the waist, stretching the rib knit to fit as you sew Fig. 10.24b.

10:6 — Revision

(1) Why don't you have to finish off the seams to prevent fraying on this top?
(2) What is the difference between the rib knit you used for the band and the single knit fabric you used for the top?
(3) What property does the rib knit have that makes it suitable for cuffs, waist bands, and neck bands?
Fabrics for rugged wear have to be strong. Try this experiment and write up the results in your workbook. Have other people assist you with the rubbing, then you will be sure that all fabrics get the same treatment. Rub in time together, and stop and start together.
(4) ***Aim:*** To find out which fabrics wear out from rubbing or abrasion.

Method

(a) Tie different pieces of fabric over metal tins.
(b) Rub back and forth across the fabric for three minutes using a pumice stone.
(c) Make sure that you use the same slow rubbing motion on each fabric.
(d) Compare the fabrics. Some will be in holes, others may not be worn at all.

Fabric name	Condition after abrasion

10:6 — Extension

(1) Find out how fleecy-lined knit fabric is made.
(2) Knit a square of rib and a square of single knit. Do these hand-knitted samples have the same properties as manufactured knit fabrics? If not, how do they differ?

Activity 10:7 — Pre-school bag

Fig. 10.25 The pre-school bag

You will need

- 0.5 m heavy unbleached calico
- Thread to match
- Brightly coloured fabric scraps
- Thread to match each fabric

Method

(1) Cut out fabric pieces for the appliqué using the following patterns.

Fig. 10.26 Appliqué design

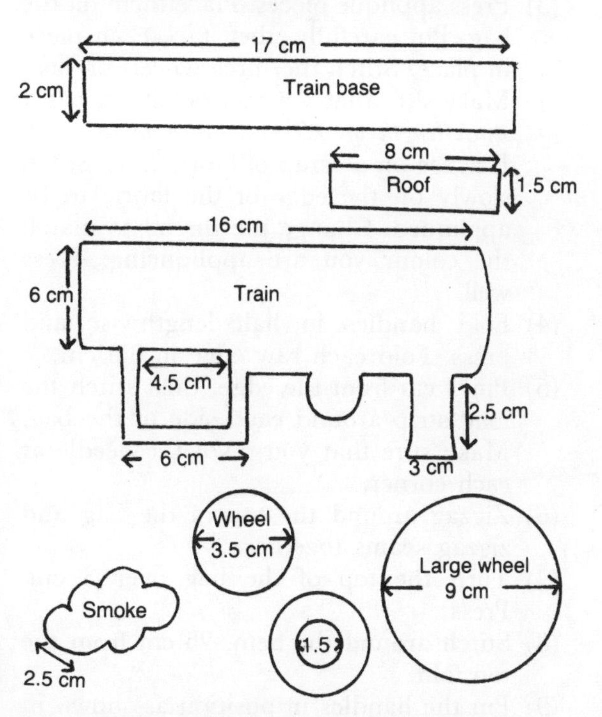

Fig. 10.27 Design pieces

(2) Cut out bag pieces using Fig. 10.27.

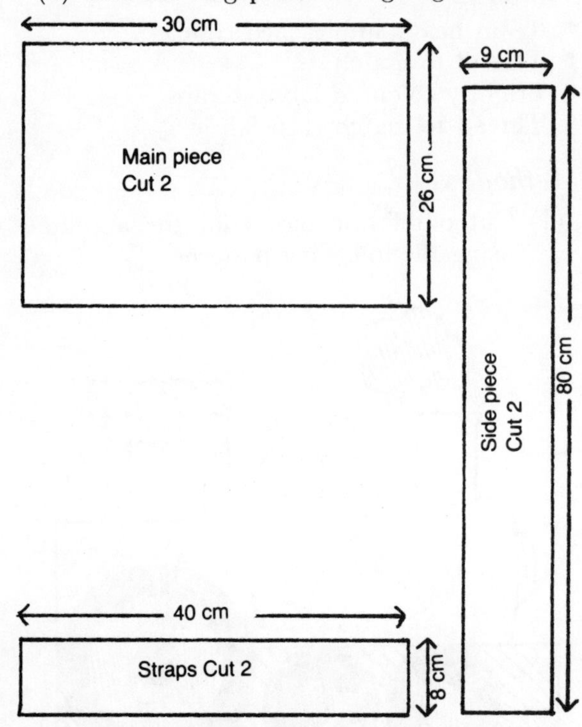

Fig. 10.28 Bag pattern pieces

(3) Press appliqué pieces. Place them on the bag. Pin carefully, then tack each piece in place. Stitch the three wheels on last. Make sure that your zigzag stitch has a *stitch length of 0.3* and *stitch width of 3.* Practise on a scrap of fabric first. Stitch slowly on the edge of the fabric to be appliquéd. Change the thread to match the colour you are appliquéing. Press well.

(4) Fold handles in half lengthwise and press. Fold each raw edge in 0.5 cm.

(5) Pin 1 cm from the edge, then stitch the long strip around each side of the bag. Make sure that you pivot the needle at each corner.

(6) Zigzag around the top of the bag and zigzag seams together.

(7) Turn the top of the bag over 3 cm. Press.

(8) Stitch around the hem, 25 cm from the top fold.

(9) Pin the handles in position as shown in Fig. 10.29.

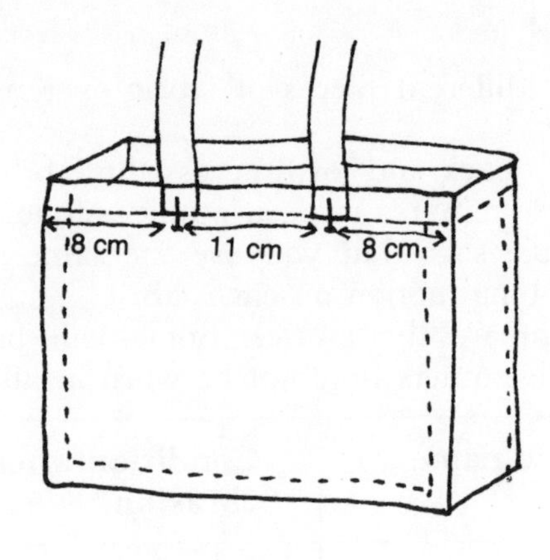

Fig. 10.29 Pinning the handles in position

(10) Stitch handles as shown in Fig. 10.30.

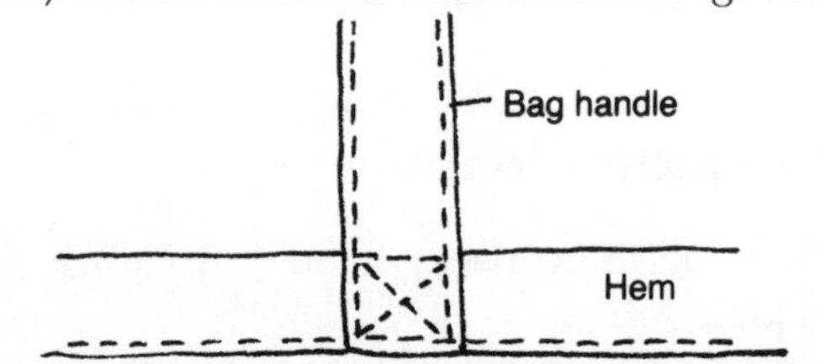

Fig. 10.30 Stitching the handles to the bag

10:7 — Revision

(1) Why is it important to choose strong, bright colours for decorating children's wear?

(2) A heavy cotton fabric like denim or strong calico is best for this article because it is hard-wearing. Try the wear test on your fabric. This test is outlined in the worksheet for the *beach top*.

(3) What uses might a small child have for this bag?

(4) Design a name tag to go on the inside of the bag. How would a child who can't read recognise their bag from another child's?

10:7 — Extension

Children's clothing must not catch fire easily. Children's night clothes must be flame resistant. Cotton and wool instead of polyester and nylon are the best fabrics for children's clothes.

(1) How would you find out if a pair of pyjamas were flameproof?
(2) Find out about the Australian Standard [AS 1248–1967] for children's nightwear. What are the guidelines for manufacturers?
(3) What are the safety requirements for children's toys set down by the Australian Standards Association [AS 1647–Part 4]?
(4) What would you do if a person's clothes caught fire?

Activity 10:8 — Plaiting a leather belt

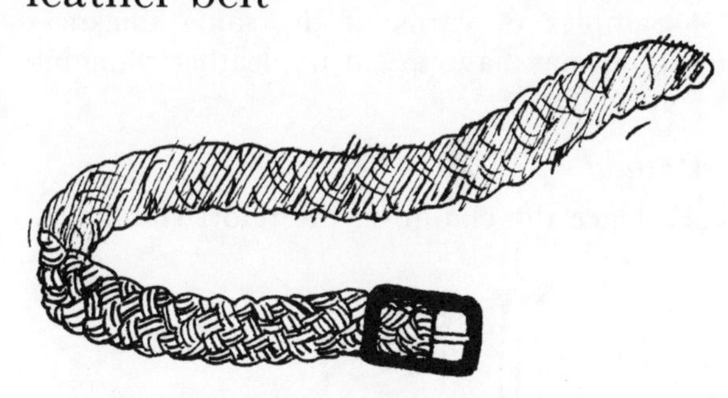

Fig. 10.31 Plaited leather belt

You will need

- 6 strands of leather thonging, each 3 m long
- Belt buckle

Method

(1) Bend each strand over at the centre
(2) Begin plaiting at the pointed end of the belt by looping two of the strands together, doubling them over at the centre (Fig. 10.32).

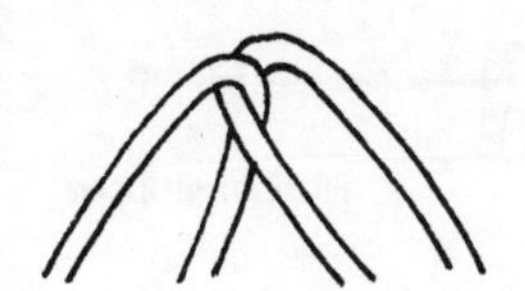

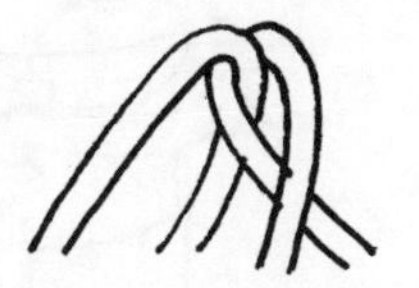

Fig. 10.32 Looping two strands together

(3) Plait the ends (Fig. 10.33).

Fig. 10.33 Plaiting the ends

(4) Introduce a new double strand (Fig. 10.34).

Fig. 10.34 Introducing a new strand

(5) Plait this strand into position (Fig. 10.35).

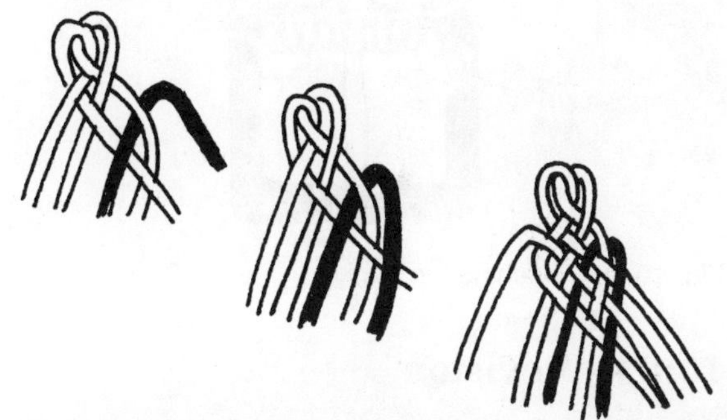

Fig. 10.35 Plaiting the new strand

(6) Continue introducing more strands in the same way until all 12 strands are in use (Fig. 10.36).

Fig. 10.36 All 12 strands in use

(7) Continue plaiting until you have a plait the length of your waist measurement plus 20 cm from the starting point. Weave the two outside strands as shown in Fig. 10.37.

Fig. 10.37 First stage of finish

(8) Loop the other strands over the buckle and darn them into the plaiting with a bodkin needle (Fig. 10.38).

Fig. 10.38 Attaching the buckle

10:8 — Revision

The craft of plaiting is considered to be even older than the ancient craft of weaving. Plaiting of an extremely high standard is still being carried on by many of the primitive tribes in different parts of the world. Natural materials are usually used such as cane, leather, and straw.

(1) What materials other than leather could you use to make this belt?
(2) What other uses does plaiting have beside making belts?
(3) Make a sample of plaiting using 5 different coloured 1.5 mm wide ribbons and paste it in your workbook.
(4) Find out how leather thonging is made. Do the following experiment to test the strength of different yarns:

Fig. 10.39 Plaiting sample

10:8 — Extension

You will need

- Retort stand and clamp
- A weight hanger and slotted weights
- Large rubber stopper
- Samples of yarns of the same thickness [you may have to cut the leather thonging in half]

Method

(1) Place the clamp on the retort stand

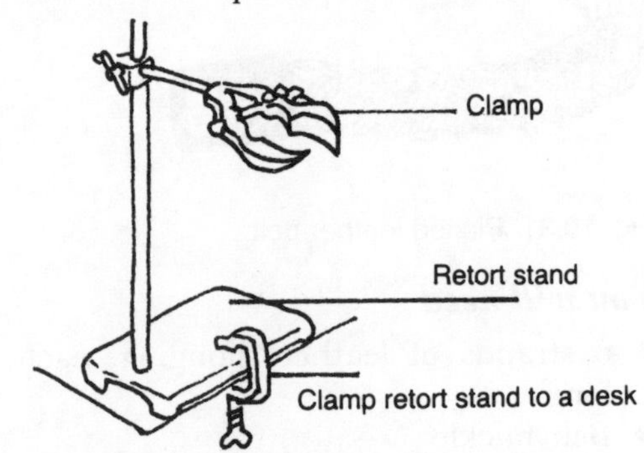

Fig. 10.40 Retort stand and clamp

(2) Put a yarn to be tested on to the rubber stopper and clamp it in place (Fig. 10.41).

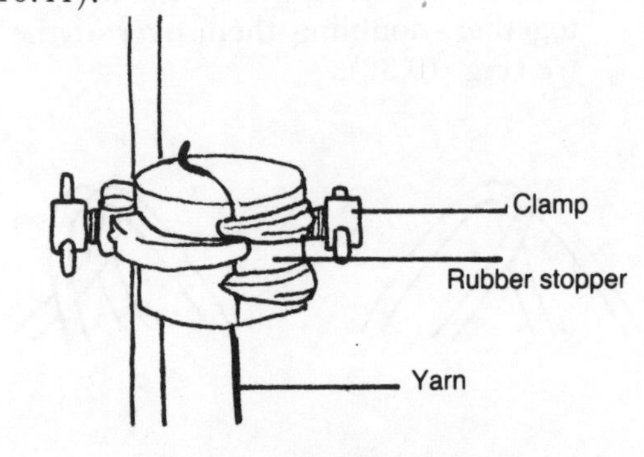

Fig. 10.41 Yarn to be tested clamped into place

(3) Tie the weight hanger on to the yarn (Fig. 10.42).

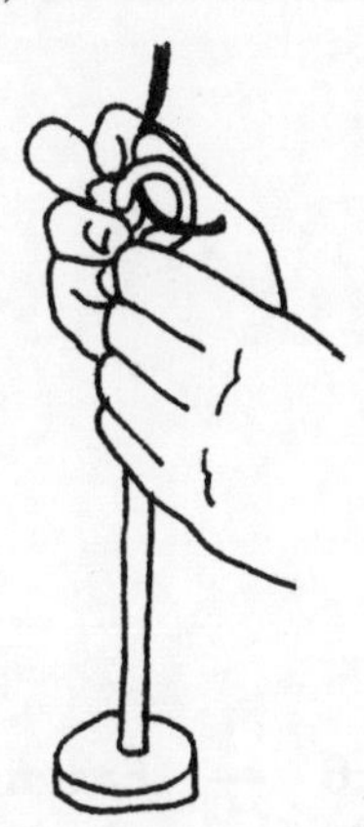

Fig. 10.42 Tying on the weight hanger

(4) Add weights 100 g at a time until the thread snaps (Fig. 10.43).

Record the total mass of the weights added when the yarn snapped in the following table:

Name of yarn	**Mass of weights when yarn snapped**

Which yarns were the strongest? Why?

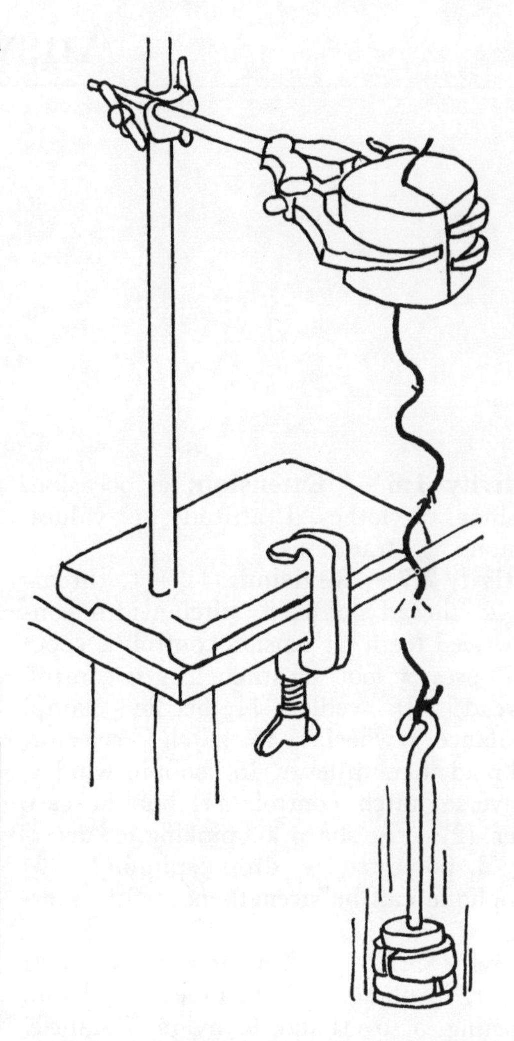

Fig. 10.43 Yarn snapping

Answers

Activity 1:6 — Extension: a. occasion, b. fashion, c. clothes, d. attitudes, e. values, f. customs, g. traditions.

Activity 2:7 — Revision: (1) — 1. throat-plate, 2. thread guide, 3. stitch width control, 4. feed teeth, 5. tension control 6. spool pin, 7. presser foot, 8. stitch length control, 9. thread, 10. needle, 11. needle clamp, 12. balance wheel, 13. stitch selector, 14. thread take-up lever, 15. bobbin winder, 16. reverse stitch control, 17. bobbin case shutter. (2) — a. sharp, b. pinking, c. detergent, d. polyester, e. drop spinning. (3) — Appliqué can be strengthened with interfacing.

Activity 3:12 — Revision crossword: *Down* 1. insulation, 2. Spandex, 3. loom, 4. twisting, 5. overhand, 6. nylon, 7. fabric, 8. bias, 9. macramé, 10. acrylic, 11. It, 12. woven, 13. grain. *Across* 1. insulation, 2. even, 3. ib, 4. bag, 5. oi, 6. nappies, 7. Lycra, 8. two, 9. weaving, 10. cosy.

Activity 4:6 — Revision: (1) — a. design, b. aesthetic, c. symbolic, d. collage, e. functional. (2) — a. plan, b. suits, c. unacceptable, d. aesthetically, e. Collage.

Activity 5:6 — Extension: 1. time, 2. catalogue, 3. tissue, 4. sewing, 5. fabric, 6. body, 7. notions, 8. nap, 9. notches, 10. arrows.

Activity 6:7 — Revision: (1) — a, b, d, b, c, b. (2) — Consumer. (3) — a. thermal, services, thinsulate, shopping, wadding, fibre. b. weight.

Activity 7:8 — Revision: (2) — Before buying clothes a wise consumer is aware of the apparel needed. (3) — a. advertising, b. consumer, c. woven, knitted, d. drape, e. cotton, linen, f. wool, g. label, h. stain.

Activity 8.3 Ⓐ 5, 6, 7, 8, 9, 10. Ⓑ 1, 2, 3, 4, 11, 12.

Activity 8:6 — Revision: (1) — a. true, true, true, b. false, c. false, d. true, e. true, f. true, g. true, h. false. (2) — Ⓐ 11, 12, 13. Ⓑ 7, 8, 14, 15, 16, 17. Ⓒ 3, 4, 5, 6, 9, 10. Ⓓ 1, 2, 18.

Activity 9:4 (2) — Mass production has meant regional clothing styles are worn only at festivals.

Index